BIG IDEAS
MATH.
Modeling Real Life

Grade 7 Advanced

Student Journal

- Review & Refresh

- Exploration Journal

- Practice Worksheets

- Notetaking with Vocabulary

- Self-Assessments

- Exploration Manipulatives

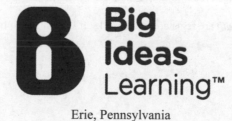

Big
Ideas
Learning™

Erie, Pennsylvania

About the Student Journal

Review & Refresh

The Review & Refresh provides students the opportunity to practice prior skills necessary to move forward.

Exploration Journal

The Exploration pages correspond to the Exploration in the Pupil Edition. Here students have room to show their work and record their answers.

Practice Worksheets

Each section of the Pupil Edition has an additional practice on the key concepts taught in the lesson.

Notetaking with Vocabulary

The student-friendly notetaking component is designed to be a reference for key vocabulary from the lesson. There is room for students to add definition to their words and take notes about key ideas.

Self-Assessment

For every lesson, students can rate their understanding of the learning target and success criteria.

Exploration Manipulatives

Manipulatives needed for the explorations are included in the back of the Student Journal.

Printed in the United States

ISBN 13: 978-1-64245-154-2

456789-22

Contents

Contents

Contents

Contents

Contents

Contents

Contents

Big Ideas Math: Modeling Real Life Grade 7 Advanced
Student Journal

ix

Contents

Contents

Contents

Contents

Name_____ Date_____

Chapter 1 Review & Refresh

Simplify the expression.

1. $18x - 6x + 2x$

2. $4b - 7 - 15b + 3$

3. $15(6 - g)$

4. $-24 + 2(y - 9)$

5. $9m + 4(12 - m)$

6. $16(a - 2) + 3(10 - a)$

7. You are selling lemonade for $1.50, a bag of kettle corn for $3, and a hot dog for $2.50 at a fair. Write and simplify an expression for the amount of money you receive when p people buy one of each item.

Big Ideas Math: Modeling Real Life Grade 7 Advanced

Chapter 1 Review & Refresh (continued)

Add or subtract.

8. $-1 + (-3)$

9. $0 + (-12)$

10. $-5 + (-3)$

11. $-4 + (-4)$

12. $5 - (-2)$

13. $-5 - 2$

14. $0 - (-6)$

15. $-9 - 3$

16. In a city, the record monthly high temperature for July is 88°F. The record monthly low temperature is 30°F. What is the range of temperatures for July?

Name_____ Date_____

 1.1 **Solving Simple Equations**
For use with Exploration 1.1

Learning Target: Write and solve one-step equations.

Success Criteria:
- I can apply properties of equality to produce equivalent equations.
- I can solve equations using addition, subtraction, multiplication, or division.
- I can use equations to model and solve real-life problems.

1 **EXPLORATION:** Using Properties of Equality

Work with a partner.

a. You have used the following properties in a previous course. Explain the meaning of each property.

- Addition Property of Equality

- Subtraction Property of Equality

- Multiplication Property of Equality

- Division Property of Equality

1.1 Solving Simple Equations (continued)

b. Which property can you use to solve each of the equations modeled by the algebra tiles? Solve each equation and explain your method.

c. Write an equation that can be solved using one property of equality. Exchange equations with another pair and find the solution.

Notetaking with Vocabulary

Vocabulary:

Notes:

 Self-Assessment

Use the scale below to rate your understanding of the learning target and the success criteria.

1	2	3	4
I do not understand.	I can do it with help.	I can do it on my own.	I can teach someone else.

	Rating	Date
1.1 Solving Simple Equations		
Learning Target: Write and solve one-step equations.	1 2 3 4	
I can apply properties of equality to produce equivalent equations.	1 2 3 4	
I can solve equations using addition, subtraction, multiplication, or division.	1 2 3 4	
I can use equations to model and solve real-life problems.	1 2 3 4	

1.1 Practice

Solve the equation. Check your solution.

1. $h + 4\pi = 30\pi$
2. $\frac{1}{6} = \frac{5}{12} + p$
3. $c - 2.3 = -5.1$

4. You shopped online and found your MP3 player for \$9.75 less than the store price p. The online price was \$64. Write and solve an equation to find the store price.

Solve the equation. Check your solution.

5. $\frac{4}{3} = \frac{2}{15} j$
6. $-23.6 = 5.9t$
7. $6\pi = -2\pi q$

8. The area of a rectangle is 55.8 square inches. The width of the rectangle is 4.5 inches. Write and solve an equation to find the length of the rectangle.

Solve the equation. Check your solution.

9. $5.6 \div 0.4 - r = -8$
10. $n - 5 \cdot \frac{2}{3} = \frac{3}{4}$

11. Write an addition equation and a multiplication equation that each have a solution of -5.

12. A fruit basket contains oranges and grapefruits. One-third of the oranges and one-fourth of the grapefruits were spoiled. You threw away 4 oranges and 7 grapefruits. How many pieces of fruit were in the basket?

13. You and two friends pay \$40 for tickets. The cost was divided three ways in the ratio $1 : 3 : 6$.

    a. How much did each person pay?

    b. What is one possible reason the money is not divided evenly?

14. Your school is raising money for a non-profit organization. The local chapter of the non-profit organization keeps 80% of the money raised, and 20% goes to the national chapter of the non-profit organization. Four of your friends each donate the same amount. The total money you raise for the local chapter of the non-profit organization is \$51.20. How much does each friend donate?

1.2 Solving Multi-Step Equations
For use with Exploration 1.2

Learning Target: Write and solve multi-step equations.

Success Criteria:
- I can apply properties to produce equivalent equations.
- I can solve multi-step equations.
- I can use multi-step equations to model and solve real-life problems.

---

1 EXPLORATION: Finding Angle Measures

Work with a partner. Find each angle measure in each figure. Use equations to justify your answers.

a.

b.

c.

d.

1.2 **Solving Multi-Step Equations** (continued)

e.

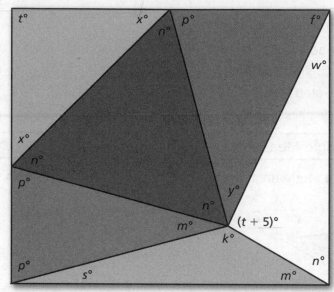

1.2 Notetaking with Vocabulary

Vocabulary:

Notes:

1.2 Self-Assessment

Use the scale below to rate your understanding of the learning target and the success criteria.

1	2	3	4
I do not understand.	I can do it with help.	I can do it on my own.	I can teach someone else.

	Rating	Date
1.2 Solving Multi-Step Equations		
Learning Target: Write and solve multi-step equations.	1 2 3 4	
I can apply properties to produce equivalent equations.	1 2 3 4	
I can solve multi-step equations.	1 2 3 4	
I can use multi-step equations to model and solve real-life problems.	1 2 3 4	

1.2 Practice

Solve the equation. Check your solution.

1. $\frac{5}{7}p - \frac{2}{7}p + 12 = 6$

2. $2.1x + 1.3x - 4.6 = 2.2$

3. $3(5 - 2h) + 9 = -30$

4. $14(x - 3) - 22x = -18$

5. The sum of the measures of the interior angles of the triangle is 180°. Write and solve an equation to find the value of the variable.

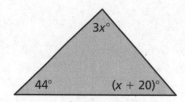

6. A rectangular field has an area of 2100 square feet. The length of the field is 50 feet.

    a. How wide is the field?

    b. The field is divided into 3 rectangles, as shown. Write and solve an equation to find x.

    c. Determine the dimensions of each rectangle.

7. You are researching the price of MP3 players. You found an average price of $58.80. One MP3 player costs $56 and another costs $62. Find the price of the third MP3 player.

8. The perimeter of a triangle is 42 inches. One side measures 18 inches. The shortest side measures x inches. The longest side measures 1 inch less than four times the length of the shortest side. Write and solve an equation to find the length of the longest side.

9. You order 4 fish sandwiches and a hamburger. The cost of the hamburger is $2.50. Your total bill before tax is $14.30. Write and solve an equation to find the cost of a fish sandwich.

10. A food service in the mall prepares free samples of chicken to give out during dinner time. One hour later, the food service has given out 4 fewer than 70% of the total number of samples. How many samples did the food service prepare if they gave out 80 samples in the first hour?

Name_____ Date_____

1.3 Solving Equations with Variables on Both Sides
For use with Exploration 1.3

Learning Target: Write and solve equations with variables on both sides.

Success Criteria:
- I can explain how to solve an equation with variables on both sides.
- I can determine whether an equation has one solution, no solution, or infinitely many solutions.
- I can use equations with variables on both sides to model and solve real-life problems.

1 EXPLORATION: Finding Missing Measures in Figures

Work with a partner.

a. If possible, find the value of x so that the value of the perimeter (in feet) is equal to the value of the area (in square feet) for each figure. Use an equation to justify your answer.

1.3 **Solving Equations with Variables on Both Sides** (continued)

b. If possible, find the value of y so that the value of the surface area (in square inches) is equal to the value of the volume (in cubic inches) for each figure. Use an equation to justify your answer.

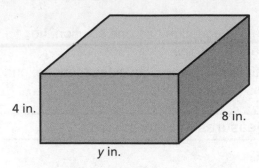

4 in.

8 in.

y in.

y in.

4 in.

4 in.

c. How are the equations you used in parts (a) and (b) different from equations used in previous sections? Explain how to solve this type of equation.

Name_____ Date_____

 Notetaking with Vocabulary

Vocabulary:

Notes:

 Self-Assessment

Use the scale below to rate your understanding of the learning target and the success criteria.

1	**2**	**3**	**4**
I do not understand.	I can do it with help.	I can do it on my own.	I can teach someone else.

	Rating	Date
1.3 Solving Equations with Variables on Both Sides		
Learning Target: Write and solve equations with variables on both sides.	1 2 3 4	
I can explain how to solve an equation with variables on both sides.	1 2 3 4	
I can determine whether an equation has one solution, no solution, or infinitely many solutions.	1 2 3 4	
I can use equations with variables on both sides to model and solve real-life problems.	1 2 3 4	

1.3 Practice

If possible, find the value of _x_ so that the value of the surface area is equal to the value of the volume.

1.

    _x_ in.

    3 in.

    10 in.

2.

    _x_ m

    4 m

    8 m

Solve the equation. Check your solution.

3. $\frac{4}{7}m = 18 - \frac{2}{7}m$

4. $4(2s - 3) = 3(s + 1)$

5. Your cellular telephone provider offers two plans. Plan A has a monthly fee of $15 and $0.25 per text. Plan B has a monthly fee of $20 and $0.05 per text. Write and solve an equation to find the number of texts than you must send to have the same cost for each of the plans.

6. Describe and correct the error in solving the equation.

    ✗ $0.4x = 0.2(x - 8)$
            $0.4x = 0.2x - 8$
            $0.2x = -8$
                $x = -4$

Solve the equation. Check your solution, if possible.

7. $4.2x - 3 = 0.5(8.4x + 6)$

8. $-\frac{1}{2}x + 1\frac{1}{2} = \frac{1}{2}(3 - x)$

9. The original price _p_ for a necklace is the same at Store A and Store B. At Store A, the sale price is 60% of the original price. Last month, at Store B, the sale price was $40 less than the original price. This month, Store B is selling the necklace for 80% of last month's reduced price, making this month's sale price at Store B equal to the sale price at Store A. Write and solve an equation to find the original price of the necklace.

10. A yoga studio charges a $36 membership fee and $20.60 per month for 10 classes. A Martial Arts studio charges a $20 membership fee and $22.20 per month for 10 classes. Your friend belongs to the yoga studio the same month you belong to the Martial Arts studio. After how many months is your friend's total cost the same as your total cost?

Name_____ Date_____

1.4 Rewriting Equations and Formulas
For use with Exploration 1.4

Learning Target: Solve literal equations for given variables and convert temperatures.

Success Criteria:
- I can use properties of equality to rewrite literal equations.
- I can use a formula to convert temperatures.

1 EXPLORATION: Rewriting Formulas

Work with a partner.

a. Write a formula for the height h of each figure. Explain your method.

- A parallelogram with area A and base b.

- A rectangular prism with volume V, length ℓ, and width w

- A triangle with area A and base b

b. Write a formula for the length ℓ of each figure. Explain your method.

- A rectangle with perimeter P and width w

- A rectangular prism with surface area S, width w, and height h

1.4   **Rewriting Equations and Formulas** (continued)

c. Use your formulas in parts (a) and (b) to find the missing dimension of each figure.

$A = 56$ m^2

h

$b = 8$ m

$w = 4$ in. $P = 19$ in.

ℓ

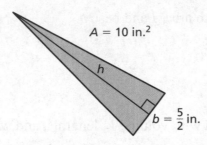

$A = 10$ in.^{2}

h

$b = \dfrac{5}{2}$ in.

$S = 108$ m^2

$h = 3$ m

$w = 4$ m

ℓ

$V = 60$ in.^{3}

h

$B = 12$ in.^{2}

1.4 Notetaking with Vocabulary

Vocabulary:

Notes:

1.4 Self-Assessment

Use the scale below to rate your understanding of the learning target and the success criteria.

1	**2**	**3**	**4**
I do not understand.	I can do it with help.	I can do it on my own.	I can teach someone else.

	Rating	Date
1.4 Rewriting Equations and Formulas		
Learning Target: Solve literal equations for given variables and convert temperatures.	1 2 3 4	
I can use properties of equality to rewrite literal equations.	1 2 3 4	
I can use a formula to convert temperatures.	1 2 3 4	

1.4 Practice

Solve the equation for y.

1. $3x - \frac{1}{4}y = -2$

2. $4.5x - 1.5y = 5.4$

3. The formula for the volume of a rectangular prism is $V = \ell wh$.

   a. Solve the formula for w.

   b. Use the new formula to find the value of w when $V = 210$ cubic feet, $\ell = 10$ feet, and $h = 3$ feet.

Solve the equation for the bold variable. Explain your method.

4. $S = \pi r^2 + 2\pi r\boldsymbol{h}$

5. $A = \frac{1}{2}P\boldsymbol{a}$

6. The formula $F = \frac{9}{5}C + 32$ converts temperatures from degrees Celsius C to degrees Fahrenheit F.

   a. Solve the formula for C.

   b. The boiling point of water is 212°F. What is the temperature in degrees Celsius?

   c. If a house thermostat is set at 80°F, what is the setting in degrees Celsius? Round your answer to the nearest tenth.

7. The formula for the area of a sector of a circle is $A = \dfrac{m}{360}\pi r^2$, given the measure m of the angle and the radius r of the circle.

   a. Solve the formula for m.

   b. Find the measure of the angle when the area of the sector is 5 square centimeters and the radius is 2 centimeters. Round your answer to the nearest tenth.

   c. If the area of the sector in part (b) is greater than 5 square centimeters, is the measure of the angle *greater than* or *less than* the answer to part (b)? Explain.

8. The formula for simple interest is $I = Prt$.

I	\$135
P	
r	6%
t	3 years

   a. Solve the formula for P.

   b. Use the new formula to find the value of P in the table.

Name_____ Date_____

Use the scale below to rate your understanding of the learning target and the success criteria.

1	2	3	4
I do not understand.	I can do it with help.	I can do it on my own.	I can teach someone else.

	Rating	Date
1.1 Solving Simple Equations		
Learning Target: Write and solve one-step equations.	1 2 3 4	
I can apply properties of equality to produce equivalent equations.	1 2 3 4	
I can solve equations using addition, subtraction, multiplication, or division.	1 2 3 4	
I can use equations to model and solve real-life problems.	1 2 3 4	
1.2 Solving Multi-Step Equations		
Learning Target: Write and solve multi-step equations.	1 2 3 4	
I can apply properties to produce equivalent equations.	1 2 3 4	
I can solve multi-step equations.	1 2 3 4	
I can use multi-step equations to model and solve real-life problems.	1 2 3 4	
1.3 Solving Equations with Variables on Both Sides		
Learning Target: Write and solve equations with variables on both sides.	1 2 3 4	
I can explain how to solve an equation with variables on both sides.	1 2 3 4	
I can determine whether an equation has one solution, no solution, or infinitely many solutions.	1 2 3 4	
I can use equations with variables on both sides to model and solve real-life problems.	1 2 3 4	

Chapter 1 **Chapter Self-Assessment** (continued)

	Rating	Date
1.4 Rewriting Equations and Formulas		
Learning Target: Solve literal equations for given variables and convert temperatures.	1 2 3 4	
I can use properties of equality to rewrite literal equations.	1 2 3 4	
I can use a formula to convert temperatures.	1 2 3 4	

Chapter 2 Review & Refresh

Reflect the point in (a) the *x*-axis and (b) the *y*-axis.

1. $(1, 1)$

2. $(-2, -4)$

3. $(-3, 3)$

4. $(4, -3)$

5. $(-1, 2)$

6. $(3, 2)$

Chapter 2 **Review & Refresh** (continued)

Draw the polygon with the given vertices in a coordinate plane.

7. $A(2, 2), B(2, 7), C(6, 7), D(6, 2)$

8. $E(3, 8), F(3, 1), G(6, 1), H(6, 8)$

9. $I(7, 6), J(5, 2), K(2, 4)$

10. $L(1, 5), M(1, 2), N(8, 2)$

11. $O(3, 7), P(6, 7), Q(9, 3), R(1, 3)$

12. $S(9, 9), T(7, 1), U(2, 4), V(4, 7)$

Name_____ Date_____

2.1 Translations
For use with Exploration 2.1

Learning Target: Translate figures in the coordinate plane.

Success Criteria:
- I can identify a translation.
- I can find the coordinates of a translated figure.
- I can use coordinates to translate a figure.

---

1 EXPLORATION: Sliding Figures

Work with a partner.

a. For each figure below, draw the figure in a coordinate plane. Then copy the figure onto a piece of transparent paper and slide the copy to a new location in the coordinate plane. Describe the location of the copy compared to the location of the original.

- point
- line segment
- line
- triangle
- rectangle

2.1 **Translations** (continued)

    b. When you slide figures, what do you notice about sides, angles, and parallel lines?

    c. Describe the location of each point below compared to the point $A(x, y)$.

$$B(x + 1, y + 2) \qquad C(x - 3, y + 4)$$

$$D(x - 2, y + 3) \qquad E(x + 4, y - 1)$$

    d. You copy a point with coordinates (x, y) and slide it horizontally a units and vertically b units. What are the coordinates of the copy?

2.1 Notetaking with Vocabulary

Vocabulary:

Notes:

2.1 Self-Assessment

Use the scale below to rate your understanding of the learning target and the success criteria.

1	2	3	4
I do not understand.	I can do it with help.	I can do it on my own.	I can teach someone else.

	Rating	Date
2.1 Translations		
Learning Target: Translate figures in the coordinate plane.	1 2 3 4	
I can identify a translation.	1 2 3 4	
I can find the coordinates of a translated figure.	1 2 3 4	
I can use coordinates to translate a figure.	1 2 3 4	

2.1 Practice

Tell whether the right figure is a translation of the left figure.

1.

2.

3. Translate the figure 5 units right and 1 unit up. What are the coordinates of the image?

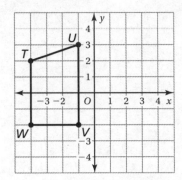

Describe the translation of the point to its image.

4. $(1, 5) \rightarrow (-1, 1)$

5. $(-2, -3) \rightarrow (-2, 4)$

6. A square is translated 3 units left and 5 units down. Then the image is translated 4 units right and 2 units down.

   a. Describe the translation of the original square to the ending position.

   b. Describe the translation of the ending position to the original square.

7. You rearrange your bedroom. Tell whether each move is an example of a translation. Explain your reasoning.

   a. You slide your bed 1 foot along the wall.

   b. You move your desk and chair to the opposite wall.

   c. You move your bed stand to the other side of the bed.

2.2 Reflections
For use with Exploration 2.2

Learning Target: Reflect figures in the coordinate plane.

Success Criteria:
- I can identify a reflection.
- I can find the coordinates of a figure reflected in an axis.
- I can use coordinates to reflect a figure in the *x*- or *y*-axis.

---

1 EXPLORATION: Reflecting Figures

Work with a partner.

a. For each figure below, draw the figure in the coordinate plane. Then copy the axes and the figure onto a piece of transparent paper. Flip the transparent paper and align the origin and the axes with the coordinate plane. For each pair of figures, describe the line of symmetry.

- point
- line segment
- line

- triangle
- rectangle

2.2 **Reflections** (continued)

    b. When you reflect figures, what do you notice about sides, angles, and parallel lines?

    c. Describe the relationship between each point below and the point $A(4, 7)$ in terms of reflections.

$$B(-4, 7) \qquad\qquad C(4, -7) \qquad\qquad D(-4, -7)$$

    d. A point with coordinates (x, y) is reflected in the x-axis. What are the coordinates of the image?

    e. Repeat part (d) when the point is reflected in the y-axis.

Notetaking with Vocabulary

Vocabulary:

Notes:

 Self-Assessment

Use the scale below to rate your understanding of the learning target and the success criteria.

1	2	3	4
I do not understand.	I can do it with help.	I can do it on my own.	I can teach someone else.

	Rating	Date
2.2 Reflections		
Learning Target: Reflect figures in the coordinate plane	1 2 3 4	
I can identify a reflection.	1 2 3 4	
I can find the coordinates of a figure reflected in an axis.	1 2 3 4	
I can use coordinates to reflect a figure in the x- or y-axis.	1 2 3 4	

Name _____   Date _____

Tell whether one figure is a reflection of the other figure.

1.

2.

Draw the figure and its reflection in the *x*-axis. Identify the coordinates of the image.

3. $K(-3, 3), L(-2, 1), M(1, 2), N(2, 5)$

4. $O(-2, -1), P(-1, -3), Q(1, -4), R(3, -1)$

Draw the figure and its reflection in the *y*-axis. Identify the coordinates of the image.

5. $B(2, -3), C(3, 1), D(5, 3), E(3, 0)$

6. $G(-5, -5), H(-3, -1), I(-2, 4), J(-1, -1)$

7. What does the word "pop" spell when it is reflected in a horizontal line?

The coordinates of a point and its image after a reflection are given. Is the reflection in the *x*-axis or *y*-axis? Explain your reasoning.

8. $(0, 3) \rightarrow (0, -3)$

9. $(1, 5) \rightarrow (-1, 5)$

10. The graph shows $\triangle JKL$.

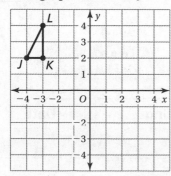

    a. Reflect the triangle in the *x*-axis. Then reflect the image in the *y*-axis. Graph the resulting triangle.

    b. If the triangle is first reflected in the *y*-axis and then reflected in the *x*-axis, how does this change the resulting triangle? Explain your reasoning.

11. $\triangle ABC$ has vertices $A(-2, -1), B(4, 2),$ and $C(2, -2)$.

    a. Reflect $\triangle ABC$ in the *x*-axis, giving $\triangle A'B'C'$. Then reflect $\triangle A'B'C'$ in the *y*-axis. What are the coordinates of the resulting triangle?

    b. How are the *x*- and *y*-coordinates of the resulting triangle related to the *x*- and *y*-coordinates of $\triangle ABC$?

Name_____ Date _____

2.3 Rotations
For use with Exploration 2.3

Learning Target: Rotate figures in the coordinate plane.

Success Criteria:
- I can identify a rotation.
- I can find the coordinates of a figure rotated about the origin.
- I can use coordinates to rotate a figure about the origin.

1 EXPLORATION: Rotating Figures

Work with a partner.

a. For each figure below, draw the figure in the coordinate plane. Then copy the axes and figure onto a piece of transparent paper. Turn the transparent paper and align the origin and the axes with the coordinate plane. For each pair of figures, describe the angle of rotation.

- point
- line segment
- line

- triangle
- rectangle

2.3 **Rotations** (continued)

b. When you rotate figures, what do you notice about sides, angles, and parallel lines?

c. Describe the relationship between each point below and the point $A(3, 6)$ in terms of rotations.

$B(-3, -6)$ $C(6, -3)$ $D(-6, 3)$

d. What are the coordinates of a point $P(x, y)$ after a rotation $90°$ counterclockwise about the origin? $180°$? $270°$?

Notetaking with Vocabulary

Vocabulary:

Notes:

 Self-Assessment

Use the scale below to rate your understanding of the learning target and the success criteria.

1	**2**	**3**	**4**
I do not understand.	I can do it with help.	I can do it on my own.	I can teach someone else.

	Rating	Date
2.3 Rotations		
Learning Target: Rotate figures in the coordinate plane.	1 2 3 4	
I can identify a rotation.	1 2 3 4	
I can find the coordinates of a figure rotated about the origin.	1 2 3 4	
I can use coordinates to rotate a figure about the origin.	1 2 3 4	

2.3 Practice

Tell whether the dashed figure is a rotation of the solid figure about the origin. If so, give the angle and direction of rotation.

1.

2.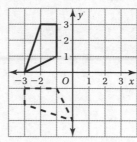

The vertices of a trapezoid are $A(1, 1), B(2, 2), C(4, 2)$, and $D(5, 1)$. Rotate the trapezoid as described. Find the coordinates of the image.

3. 90° clockwise about the origin

4. 270° counterclockwise about the origin

5. 90° clockwise about vertex A

6. 180° about vertex D

Determine whether the figure has rotational symmetry. Explain your reasoning.

7.

8.

9. You rotate a triangle 270° counterclockwise about the origin. Then you translate its image 2 units right and 1 unit down. The vertices of the final image are $(0, 2), (8, -1)$, and $(5, -2)$. What are the vertices of the original triangle?

Name_____ Date_____

Learning Target: Understand the concept of congruent figures.

Success Criteria:
- I can identify congruent figures.
- I can describe a sequence of rigid motions between two congruent figures.

1 EXPLORATION: Transforming Figures

Work with a partner.

a. For each pair of figures whose vertices are given below, draw the figures in a coordinate plane. Then copy one of the figures onto a piece of transparent paper. Use transformations to try to obtain one of the figures from the other figure.

- $A(-5, 1), B(-5, -4), C(-2, -4)$ and $D(1, 4), E(1, -1), F(-2, -1)$

- $G(1, 2), H(2, -6), J(5, 0)$ and $L(-1, -2), M(-2, 6), N(-5, 0)$

- $P(0, 0), Q(2, 2), R(4, -2)$ and $X(0, 0), Y(3, 3), Z(6, -3)$

- $A(0, 4), B(3, 8), C(6, 4), D(3, 0)$ and
  $F(-4, -3), G(-8, 0), H(-4, 3), J(0, 0)$

- $P(-2, 1), Q(-1, -2), R(1, -2), S(1, 1)$ and
  $W(7, 1), X(5, -2), Y(3, -2), Z(3, 1)$

2.4 **Congruent Figures** (continued)

b. Which pairs of figures in part (a) are identical? Explain your reasoning.

c. Figure A and Figure B are identical. Do you think there must be a sequence
of transformations that obtains Figure A from Figure B? Explain your
reasoning.

Name_____ Date_____

 2.4 Notetaking with Vocabulary

Vocabulary:

Notes:

2.4 Self-Assessment

Use the scale below to rate your understanding of the learning target and the success criteria.

1	*2*	*3*	*4*
I do not understand.	I can do it with help.	I can do it on my own.	I can teach someone else.

	Rating	Date
2.4 Congruent Figures		
Learning Target: Understand the concept of congruent figures.	1 2 3 4	
I can identify congruent figures.	1 2 3 4	
I can describe a sequence of rigid motions between two congruent figures.	1 2 3 4	

2.4 Practice

The figures are congruent. Name the corresponding angles and the corresponding sides.

1.

2.

3. The figures are congruent.

   a. What is the length of side *CD*?

   b. Which angle of *KLMN* corresponds to ∠*B*?

   c. What is the perimeter of *KLMN*?

4. The pentagons are congruent. Determine whether the statement is *true* or *false*. Explain your reasoning.

   a. ∠*B* is congruent to ∠*C*.

   b. Side *MN* is congruent to side *AE*.

   c. ∠*B* corresponds to ∠*O*.

   d. Side *BC* is congruent to side *PO*.

   e. The sum of the angle measures of *LMNOP* is 540°.

   f. The measure of ∠*B* is 120°.

5. △*JKL* is congruent to △*PQR*. Describe a sequence of rigid motions between the figures.

2.5 Dilations
For use with Exploration 2.5

Learning Target: Dilate figures in the coordinate plane.

Success Criteria:
- I can identify a dilation.
- I can find the coordinates of a figure dilated with respect to the origin.
- I can use coordinates to dilate a figure with respect to the origin.

---

1 EXPLORATION: Dilating a Polygon

Work with a partner. Use geometry software.

a. Draw a polygon in the coordinate plane. Then *dilate* the polygon with respect to the origin. Describe the scale factor of the image.

b. Compare the image and the original polygon in part (a). What do you notice about the sides? the angles?

2.5 **Dilations** (continued)

c. Describe the relationship between each point below and the point $A(x, y)$ in terms of dilations.

$B(3x, 3y)$ $\qquad\qquad\qquad$ $C(5x, 5y)$ $\qquad\qquad\qquad$ $D(0.5x, 0.5y)$

d. What are the coordinates of a point $P(x, y)$ after a dilation with respect to the origin by a scale factor of k?

2.5 Notetaking with Vocabulary

Vocabulary:

Notes:

2.5 Self-Assessment

Use the scale below to rate your understanding of the learning target and the success criteria.

1	2	3	4
I do not understand.	I can do it with help.	I can do it on my own.	I can teach someone else.

	Rating	Date
2.5 Dilations		
Learning Target: Dilate figures in the coordinate plane.	1 2 3 4	
I can identify a dilation.	1 2 3 4	
I can find the coordinates of a figure dilated with respect to the origin.	1 2 3 4	
I can use coordinates to dilate a figure with respect to the origin.	1 2 3 4	

Big Ideas Math: Modeling Real Life Grade 7 Advanced **41**
Student Journal

2.5 Practice

Tell whether the dashed figure is a dilation of the solid figure.

1.

2.

The vertices of a figure are given. Draw the figure and its image after a dilation with the given scale factor. Identify the type of dilation.

3. $A(3,-1), B(-4,4), C(-2,-3); k=5$

4. $D(10,20), E(-35,10), F(25,-30), G(5,-20); k=\frac{1}{5}$

The dashed figure is a dilation of the solid figure. Identify the type of dilation and find the scale factor. Explain your reasoning.

5.

6.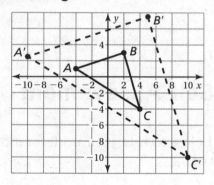

7. A scale factor of 2 is used to find the dilation of a quadrilateral.

   a. What is the sum of the angles in the original quadrilateral?

   b. What is the sum of the angles of the image after the dilation?

   c. What is the difference between the perimeter of the original figure and the perimeter of the image?

8. A triangle is dilated using a scale factor of $\frac{1}{2}$. The image is then dilated using a scale factor of $\frac{1}{3}$. What scale factor could you use to dilate the original triangle to get the final image?

9. A triangle has an area of 3. The triangle is dilated using a scale factor of 3. What is the area of the image after the dilation? Explain your reasoning.

2.6 Similar Figures
For use with Exploration 2.6

Learning Target: Understand the concept of similar figures.

Success Criteria:
- I can identify similar figures.
- I can describe a similarity transformation between two similar figures.

1 EXPLORATION: Transforming Figures

Work with a partner. Use geometry software.

a. For each pair of figures whose vertices are given below, draw the figures in a coordinate plane. Use dilations and rigid motions to try to obtain one of the figures from the other figure.

- $A(-3, 6), B(0, -3), C(3, 6)$ and $G(-1, 2), H(0, -1), J(1, 2)$

- $D(0, 0), E(3, 0), F(3, 3)$ and $L(0, 0), M(0, 6), N(-6, 6)$

- $P(1, 0), Q(4, 2), R(7, 0)$ and $X(-1, 0), Y(-4, 6), Z(-7, 0)$

- $A(-3, 2), B(-1, 2), C(-1, -1), D(-3, -1)$ and
  $F(6, 4), G(2, 4), H(2, -2), J(6, -2)$

- $P(-2, 2), Q(-1, -1), R(1, -1), S(2, 2)$ and
  $W(2, 8), X(3, 3), Y(7, 3), Z(8, 8)$

2.6 **Similar Figures** (continued)

b. Is a scale drawing represented by any of the pairs of figures in part (a)? Explain your reasoning.

c. Figure A is a scale drawing of Figure B. Do you think there must be a sequence of transformations that obtains Figure A from Figure B? Explain your reasoning.

2.6 Notetaking with Vocabulary

Vocabulary:

Notes:

2.6 Self-Assessment

Use the scale below to rate your understanding of the learning target and the success criteria.

1	2	3	4
I do not understand.	I can do it with help.	I can do it on my own.	I can teach someone else.

	Rating	Date
2.6 Similar Figures		
Learning Target: Understand the concept of similar figures.	1 2 3 4	
I can identify similar figures.	1 2 3 4	
I can describe a similarity transformation between two similar figures.	1 2 3 4	

2.6 Practice

1. Draw the figures with the given vertices in a coordinate plane. Which figures are similar? Explain your reasoning.

   Rectangle A: $(0, 0), (3, 0), (3, 2), (0, 2)$

   Rectangle B: $(0, 0), (1, 0), (1, 3), (0, 3)$

   Rectangle C: $(0, 0), (2, 0), (2, -3), (0, -3)$

2. A rectangular index card is 6 inches long and 4 inches wide. A rectangular note card is 1.5 inches long and 1 inch wide. Are the cards similar?

The two parallelograms are similar. Find the degree measure of the angle. Explain your reasoning.

3. $\angle A$

4. $\angle H$

5. $\angle D$

6. $\angle F$

7. Is it possible for the following figures to be similar? Explain.

   a. A stop sign and a speed limit sign

   b. A cell phone and a test paper

   c. A yield sign and a home plate

   d. A laptop and a swimming pool

8. Can you draw two triangles each having two 45° angles and one 90° angle that are *not* similar? Justify your answer.

9. You have a triangle that has side lengths of 6, 9, and 12.

   a. Give the side lengths of a similar triangle that is smaller than the given triangle. Justify your answer.

   b. Give the side lengths of a similar triangle that is larger than the given triangle. Justify your answer.

   c. Each side length is increased by 30%. What are the side lengths of the new triangle? Is the new triangle similar to the original triangle?

2.7 Perimeters and Areas of Similar Figures
For use with Exploration 2.7

Learning Target: Find perimeters and areas of similar figures.

Success Criteria:
- I can use corresponding side lengths to compare perimeters of similar figures.
- I can use corresponding side lengths to compare areas of similar figures.
- I can use similar figures to solve real-life problems involving perimeter and area.

---

1 EXPLORATION: Comparing Similar Figures

Work with a partner. Draw a rectangle in the coordinate plane.

a. Dilate your rectangle using each indicated scale factor k. Then complete the table for the perimeter P of each rectangle. Describe the pattern.

Original Side Lengths	$k = 2$	$k = 3$	$k = 4$	$k = 5$	$k = 6$
$P =$ ___					

b. Compare the ratios of the perimeters to the ratios of the corresponding side lengths. What do you notice?

2.7 **Perimeters and Areas of Similar Figures** (continued)

c. Repeat part (a) to complete the table for the area A of each rectangle. Describe the pattern.

Original Side Lengths	$k = 2$	$k = 3$	$k = 4$	$k = 5$	$k = 6$
$A = $ ___					

d. Compare the ratios of the areas to the ratios of the corresponding side lengths. What do you notice?

e. The rectangles shown are similar. You know the perimeter and the area of the large rectangle and a pair of corresponding side lengths. How can you find the perimeter of the small rectangle? the area of the small rectangle?

Notetaking with Vocabulary

Vocabulary:

Notes:

 Self-Assessment

Use the scale below to rate your understanding of the learning target and the success criteria.

1	2	3	4
I do not understand.	I can do it with help.	I can do it on my own.	I can teach someone else.

	Rating	Date
2.7 Perimeters and Areas of Similar Figures		
Learning Target: Find perimeters and areas of similar figures.	1　2　3　4	
I can use corresponding side lengths to compare perimeters of similar figures.	1　2　3　4	
I can use corresponding side lengths to compare areas of similar figures.	1　2　3　4	
I can use similar figures to solve real-life problems involving perimeter and area.	1　2　3　4	

2.7 Practice

1. The two figures are similar. Find the ratio (small to large) of the perimeters and of the areas.

2. The figures are similar. The ratio of the perimeters is 12 : 7. Find x.

3. The ratio of the corresponding side lengths of two similar parallelogram signs is 9 : 14.

   a. What is the ratio of the perimeters? Explain.

   b. What is the ratio of the areas? Explain.

   c. One side length of the smaller sign is 45 feet. What is the side length of the corresponding side of the larger sign?

4. A window is put in a door. The window and the door are similar rectangles. The door has a width of 4 feet. The window has a width of 30 inches.

   a. How many times greater is the area of the door than the area of the window?

   b. The area of the door is 32 square feet. What is the area of the window?

   c. What is the perimeter of the window?

5. The area of Circle P is 4π. The area of Circle Q is 25π.

   a. What is the ratio of their areas?

   b. What is the ratio of their radii? Justify your reasoning.

   c. The radius of Circle Q is decreased by 50%. What is the new circumference of Circle Q?

Chapter 2 · Chapter Self-Assessment

Use the scale below to rate your understanding of the learning target and the success criteria.

1	2	3	4
I do not understand.	I can do it with help.	I can do it on my own.	I can teach someone else.

	Rating	Date
2.1 Translations		
Learning Target: Translate figures in the coordinate plane.	1 2 3 4	
I can identify a translation.	1 2 3 4	
I can find the coordinates of a translated figure.	1 2 3 4	
I can use coordinates to translate a figure.	1 2 3 4	
2.2 Reflections		
Learning Target: Reflect figures in the coordinate plane.	1 2 3 4	
I can identify a reflection.	1 2 3 4	
I can find the coordinates of a figure reflected in an axis.	1 2 3 4	
I can use coordinates to reflect a figure in the x- or y-axis.	1 2 3 4	
2.3 Rotations		
Learning Target: Rotate figures in the coordinate plane.	1 2 3 4	
I can identify a rotation.	1 2 3 4	
I can find the coordinates of a figure rotated about the origin.	1 2 3 4	
I can use coordinates to rotate a figure about the origin.	1 2 3 4	

Chapter 2 — Chapter Self-Assessment (continued)

	Rating	Date
2.4 Congruent Figures		
Learning Target: Understand the concept of congruent figures.	1 2 3 4	
I can identify congruent figures.	1 2 3 4	
I can describe a sequence of rigid motions between two congruent figures.	1 2 3 4	
2.5 Dilations		
Learning Target: Dilate figures in the coordinate plane.	1 2 3 4	
I can identify a dilation.	1 2 3 4	
I can find the coordinates of a figure dilated with respect to the origin.	1 2 3 4	
I can use coordinates to dilate a figure with respect to the origin.	1 2 3 4	
2.6 Similar Figures		
Learning Target: Understand the concept of similar figures.	1 2 3 4	
I can identify similar figures.	1 2 3 4	
I can describe a similarity transformation between two similar figures.	1 2 3 4	
2.7 Perimeters and Areas of Similar Figures		
Learning Target: Find perimeters and areas of similar figures.	1 2 3 4	
I can use corresponding side lengths to compare perimeters of similar figures.	1 2 3 4	
I can use corresponding side lengths to compare areas of similar figures.	1 2 3 4	
I can use similar figures to solve real-life problems involving perimeter and area.	1 2 3 4	

Chapter 3 **Review & Refresh**

Tell whether the angles are *adjacent* or *vertical*. Then find the value of *x*.

1.

$x°$

$128°$

2.

$x°$

$35°$

3.

$75°$

$(2x + 1)°$

4.

$4x°$

$2x°$

5. The tree is tilted 14°. Find the value of *x*.

$14°$

$x°$

Tell whether the angles are *complementary* or *supplementary*. Then find the value of *x*.

6.

117° *x*°

7.

69°
x°

8.

41°
x°

9.

110° 5*x*°

10. A tributary joins a river at an angle. Find the value of *x*.

x°   127°

3.1 Parallel Lines and Transversals
For use with Exploration 3.1

Learning Target: Find missing angle measures created by the intersections of lines.

Success Criteria:
- I can identify congruent angles when a transversal intersects parallel lines.
- I can find angle measures when a transversal intersects parallel lines.

---

1 EXPLORATION: Exploring Intersections of Lines

Work with a partner. Use geometry software and the lines _A_ and _B_ shown.

a. Are line _A_ and line _B_ parallel? Explain your reasoning.

b. Draw a line _C_ that intersects both line _A_ and line _B_. What do you notice about the measures of the angles that are created?

3.1 **Parallel Lines and Transversals** (continued)

c. Rotate line *A* or line *B* until the angles created by the intersection of line *A* and line *C* are congruent to the angles created by the intersection of line *B* and line *C*. What do you notice about line *A* and line *B*?

d. Rotate line *C* to create different angle measures. Are the angles that were congruent in part (c) still congruent?

e. Make a conjecture about the measures of the angles created when a line intersects two parallel lines.

3.1 Notetaking with Vocabulary

Vocabulary:

Notes:

3.1 Self-Assessment

Use the scale below to rate your understanding of the learning target and the success criteria.

1	**2**	**3**	**4**
I do not understand.	I can do it with help.	I can do it on my own.	I can teach someone else.

	Rating	Date
3.1 Parallel Lines and Transversals		
Learning Target: Find missing angle measures created by the intersections of lines.	1 2 3 4	
I can identify congruent angles when a transversal intersects parallel lines.	1 2 3 4	
I can find angle measures when a transversal intersects parallel lines.	1 2 3 4	

3.1 Practice

Use the figure to find the measures of the numbered angles. Explain your reasoning.

1.

2.

Complete the statement. Explain your reasoning.

3. If the measure of ∠1 = 130°, then the measure of ∠8 = ____.

4. If the measure of ∠5 = 53°, then the measure of ∠3 = ____.

5. If the measure of ∠7 = 71°, then the measure of ∠3 = ____.

6. If the measure of ∠4 = 65°, then the measure of ∠6 = ____.

Using the diagram for angle placement only (the measurement of the angles may change), indicate if the following statements are *always*, *sometimes*, or *never* true. Explain.

7. ∠1 is congruent to ∠3.

8. ∠6 is supplementary to ∠8.

9. ∠2 is complementary to ∠1.

10. ∠8 and ∠5 are vertical angles.

11. ∠2 is congruent to ∠8.

12. If a transversal intersects two parallel lines, is it possible for all of the angles formed to be acute angles? Explain.

3.2 Angles of Triangles
For use with Exploration 3.2

Learning Target: Understand properties of interior and exterior angles of triangles.

Success Criteria:
- I can use equations to find missing angle measures of triangles.
- I can use interior and exterior angles of a triangle to solve real-life problems.

---

1 EXPLORATION: Exploring Interior and Exterior Angles of Triangles

Work with a partner.

a. Draw several triangles using geometry software. What can you conclude about the sums of the angle measures?

b. You can extend one side of a triangle to form an *exterior angle,* as shown.

exterior angle

Use geometry software to draw a triangle and an exterior angle. Compare the measure of the exterior angle with the measures of the interior angles. Repeat this process for several different triangles. What can you conclude?

3.2 Angles of Triangles (continued)

2 EXPLORATION: Using Parallel Lines and Transversals

Work with a partner. Describe what is shown in the figure below. Then use what you know about parallel lines and transversals to justify your conclusions in Exploration 1.

Notetaking with Vocabulary

Vocabulary:

Notes:

 Self-Assessment

Use the scale below to rate your understanding of the learning target and the success criteria.

1	**2**	**3**	**4**
I do not understand.	I can do it with help.	I can do it on my own.	I can teach someone else.

	Rating	Date
3.2 Angles of Triangles		
Learning Target: Understand properties of interior and exterior angles of triangles.	1 2 3 4	
I can use equations to find missing angle measures of triangles.	1 2 3 4	
I can use interior and exterior angles of a triangle to solve real-life problems.	1 2 3 4	

Name _____ Date _____

3.2 Practice

Find the measure of the interior angles of the triangle.

1.

2.

Find the measure of the exterior angle.

3.

4.

5. The ratio of the interior angle measures of a triangle is 1 : 4 : 5. What are the angle measures?

6. A right triangle has an exterior angle with a measure of 160°. Can you determine the measures of the interior angles? Explain.

7. You are in a sailboat race. The course is triangular, racing A – B – C – Finish. By what angle do the sailboats need to change so that they can make it to the finish line?

Determine whether the statement is *always*, *sometimes*, or *never* true. Explain your reasoning.

8. The exterior angles of an equilateral triangle all have the same measure.

9. All equilateral triangles have exterior angles with the same measures.

10. A triangle has two vertices with an obtuse exterior angle.

Name_____ Date_____

3.3 Angles of Polygons
For use with Exploration 3.3

Learning Target: Find interior angle measures of polygons.

Success Criteria:
- I can explain how to find the sum of the interior angle measures of a polygon.
- I can use an equation to find an interior angle measure of a polygon.
- I can find the interior angle measures of a regular polygon.

---

1 EXPLORATION: Exploring Interior Angles of Polygons

Work with a partner. In parts (a)-(f), use what you know about the interior angle measures of triangles to find the sum of the interior angle measures of each figure.

a.

b.

c.

d.

3.3 **Angles of Polygons** (continued)

e.

f.

g. Use your results in parts (a)–(f) to complete the table. Then write an equation that represents the sum S of the interior angle measures of a polygon with n sides.

Number of Sides, n	3	4	5	6	7	8	9
Number of Triangles							
Interior Angle Sum, S							

Name_____ Date_____

 Notetaking with Vocabulary

Vocabulary:

Notes:

3.3 **Self-Assessment**

Use the scale below to rate your understanding of the learning target and the success criteria.

1	2	3	4
I do not understand.	I can do it with help.	I can do it on my own.	I can teach someone else.

	Rating	Date
3.3 Angles of Polygons		
Learning Target: Find interior angle measures of polygons	1 2 3 4	
I can explain how to find the sum of the interior angle measures of a polygon.	1 2 3 4	
I can use an equation to find an interior angle measure of a polygon.	1 2 3 4	
I can find the interior angle measures of a regular polygon.	1 2 3 4	

Name_____ Date _____

Use triangles to find the sum of the interior angle measures of the polygon.

1.

2.

Find the sum of the interior angle measures of the polygon.

3.

4.

Find the value of x.

5.

6.

7. The interior angles of a regular polygon each measure 135°. How many sides does the polygon have?

8. Home plate at a baseball field is in the shape of a pentagon. Three of the interior angles are right angles, the other two angles have equal measures. What are the measures of the interior angles of home plate?

9. A Ferris wheel at a carnival is in the shape of a regular dodecagon, a twelve-sided figure.

   a. What is the sum of the interior angles of the Ferris wheel?

   b. What is the measure of each interior angle of the Ferris wheel?

3.4 Using Similar Triangles
For use with Exploration 3.4

Learning Target: Use similar triangles to find missing measures.

Success Criteria:
- I can use angle measures to determine whether triangles are similar.
- I can use similar triangles to solve real-life problems.

1 EXPLORATION: Drawing Triangles Given Two Angle Measures

Work with a partner. Use geometry software.

a. Draw a triangle that has a 50° angle and a 30° angle. Then draw a triangle that is either larger or smaller that has the same two angle measures. Are the triangles congruent? similar? Explain your reasoning.

b. Choose any two angle measures whose sum is less than 180°. Repeat part (a) using the angle measures you chose.

c. Compare your results in parts (a) and (b) with other pairs of students. Make a conjecture about two triangles that have two pairs of congruent angles.

3.4 **Using Similar Triangles** (continued)

2 **EXPLORATION:** Using Indirect Measurement

Work with a partner. Use the fact that two rays from the Sun are parallel to make a plan for how to find the height of the flagpole. Explain your reasoning.

3.4 **Notetaking with Vocabulary**

Vocabulary:

Notes:

3.4 **Self-Assessment**

Use the scale below to rate your understanding of the learning target and
the success criteria.

1	**2**	**3**	**4**
I do not understand.	I can do it with help.	I can do it on my own.	I can teach someone else.

	Rating	Date
3.4 Using Similar Triangles		
Learning Target: Use similar triangles to find missing measures.	1 2 3 4	
I can use angle measures to determine whether triangles are similar.	1 2 3 4	
I can use similar triangles to solve real-life problems.	1 2 3 4	

Name _____ Date _____

Tell whether the triangles are similar. Explain.

1.

2.

3. The triangles are similar. Find the value of x.

4. You can use indirect measurement to estimate the height of a flag pole. First measure your distance from the base of the flag pole and the distance from the ground to a point on the flag pole that you are looking at. Maintaining the same angle of sight, move back until the top of the flag pole is in your line of sight.

   a. Explain why $\triangle ABC$ and $\triangle DBE$ are similar.

   b. What is the height of the flag pole?

5. You are on a boat in the ocean, at Point A. You locate a lighthouse at Point D, beyond the line of sight of the marker at point C. You drive 0.2 mile west to Point B and then 0.1 mile south to Point C. You drive 0.3 mile more to arrive at Point E, which is due east of the lighthouse.

   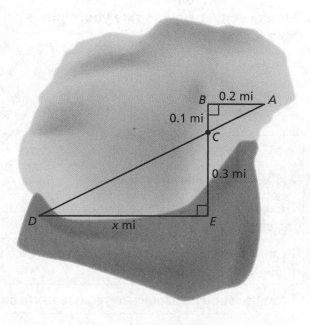

   a. Explain why $\triangle ABC$ and $\triangle DEC$ are similar.

   b. What is the distance from Point E to the lighthouse?

Chapter 3 Chapter Self-Assessment

Use the scale below to rate your understanding of the learning target and the success criteria.

1	**2**	**3**	**4**
I do not understand.	I can do it with help.	I can do it on my own.	I can teach someone else.

	Rating	Date
3.1 Parallel Lines and Transversals		
Learning Target: Find missing angle measures created by the intersections of lines.	1 2 3 4	
I can identify congruent angles when a transversal intersects parallel lines.	1 2 3 4	
I can find angle measures when a transversal intersects parallel lines.	1 2 3 4	
3.2 Angles of Triangles		
Learning Target: Understand properties of interior and exterior angles of triangles.	1 2 3 4	
I can use equations to find missing angle measures of triangles.	1 2 3 4	
I can use interior and exterior angles of a triangle to solve real-life problems.	1 2 3 4	
3.3 Angles of Polygons		
Learning Target: Find interior angle measures of polygons.	1 2 3 4	
I can explain how to find the sum of the interior angle measures of a polygon.	1 2 3 4	
I can use an equation to find an interior angle measure of a polygon.	1 2 3 4	
I can find the interior angle measures of a regular polygon.	1 2 3 4	

Chapter 3 Chapter Self-Assessment (continued)

	Rating	Date
3.4 Using Similar Triangles		
Learning Target: Use similar triangles to find missing measures.	1　2　3　4	
I can use angle measures to determine whether triangles are similar.	1　2　3　4	
I can use similar triangles to solve real-life problems.	1　2　3　4	

Chapter 4 — Review & Refresh

Evaluate the expression when $x = \frac{1}{2}$ and $y = -5$.

1. $-2xy$

2. $4x^2 - 3y$

3. $\dfrac{10y}{12x+4}$

4. $11x - 8(x - y)$

Evaluate the expression when $a = -9$ and $b = -4$.

5. $3ab$

6. $a^2 - 2(b + 12)$

7. $\dfrac{4b^2}{3b-7}$

8. $7b^2 + 5(ab - 6)$

9. You go to the movies with five friends. You and one of your friends each buy a ticket and a bag of popcorn. The rest of your friends buy just one ticket each. The expression $4x + 2(x + y)$ represents the situation. Evaluate the expression when tickets cost $7.25 and a bag of popcorn costs $3.25.

Chapter 4 Review & Refresh (continued)

Use the graph to answer the question.

10. Write the ordered pair that corresponds to Point *D*.

11. Write the ordered pair that corresponds to Point *H*.

12. Which point is located at $(-2, 4)$?

13. Which point is located at $(0, 3)$?

14. Which point(s) are located in Quadrant IV?

15. Which point(s) are located in Quadrant III?

Plot the point.

16. $(3, -1)$

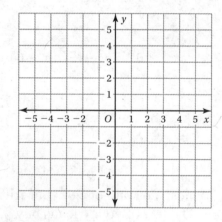

17. $(0, 2)$

18. $(-5, -4)$

19. $(-1, 0)$

20. $(-2, 3)$

4.1 Graphing Linear Equations
For use with Exploration 4.1

Learning Target: Graph linear equations.

Success Criteria:
- I can create a table of values and write ordered pairs given a linear equation.
- I can plot ordered pairs to create a graph of a linear equation.
- I can use a graph of a linear equation to solve a real-life problem.

---

1 EXPLORATION: Creating Graphs

Work with a partner. It starts snowing at midnight in Town A and Town B. The snow falls at a rate of 1.5 inches per hour.

a. In Town A, there is no snow on the ground at midnight. How deep is the snow at each hour between midnight and 6 A.M.? Make a graph that represents this situation.

Time (hours)

b. Repeat part (a) for Town B, which has 4 inches of snow on the ground at midnight.

4.1 **Graphing Linear Equations** (continued)

c. The equations below represent the depth y (in inches) of snow x hours after midnight in Town C and Town D. Graph each equation.

Town C
$y = 2x + 3$

Town D
$y = 8$

d. Use your graphs to compare the snowfalls in each town.

Name_____ Date_____

 4.1 Notetaking with Vocabulary

Vocabulary:

Notes:

4.1 Self-Assessment

Use the scale below to rate your understanding of the learning target and the success criteria.

1	2	3	4
I do not understand.	I can do it with help.	I can do it on my own.	I can teach someone else.

	Rating	Date
4.1 Graphing Linear Equations		
Learning Target: Graph linear equations.	1 2 3 4	
I can create a table of values and write ordered pairs given a linear equation.	1 2 3 4	
I can plot ordered pairs to create a graph of a linear equation.	1 2 3 4	
I can use a graph of a linear equation to solve a real-life problem.	1 2 3 4	

4.1 Practice

Graph the linear equation.

1. $y = 3.5$

2. $y = \frac{2}{3}x - 2$

3. $y = \frac{10}{3}x$

4. $y = -\frac{x}{2} + \frac{3}{2}$

5. The equation $y = 1.5x + 35$ represents the cost y (in dollars) of the family meal when the food costs \$35 and x beverages are purchased.

   a. Graph the equation.

   b. Use the graph to estimate the cost of the family meal when 5 beverages are purchased.

   c. Use the equation to find the exact cost of the family meal when 5 beverages are purchased.

Solve for y. Then graph the equation.

6. $2y + 3x = -6$

7. $x + 0.25y = 1.5$

8. There are 10 coconuts at the base of your tree. The coconuts are falling off the tree at a rate of 6 coconuts per week. Assume that you do not pick up any coconuts.

   a. Write and graph a linear equation that represents the number of coconuts at the base of your tree after x weeks.

   b. The tree will have no coconuts on it when there are 52 coconuts at the base of the tree. After how many weeks will this occur?

9. The sum s of the first n positive integers is $s = \frac{1}{2}n(n + 1)$.

   a. Plot four points (n, s) that satisfy the equation. Is the equation a linear equation? Explain your reasoning.

   b. Does the value $n = 4.2$ make sense in the context of the problem? Explain your reasoning.

10. The equation $y = 5.50x$ represents the cost y (in dollars) for x visits to the science museum in a month. Graph the linear equation. What does the graph tell you about your purchase plan with the science museum?

4.2 Slope of a Line
For use with Exploration 4.2

Learning Target: Find and interpret the slope of a line.

Success Criteria:
- I can explain the meaning of slope.
- I can find the slope of a line.
- I can interpret the slope of a line in a real-life problem.

1 EXPLORATION: Measuring the Steepness of a Line

Work with a partner. Draw any nonvertical line in a coordinate plane.

a. Develop a way to measure the *steepness* of the line. Compare your method with other pairs.

b. Draw a line that is parallel to your line. What can you determine about the steepness of each line? Explain your reasoning.

4.2 **Slope of a Line** (continued)

---

2 **EXPLORATION: Using Right Triangles**

Work with a partner. Use the figure shown.

a. $\triangle ABC$ is a right triangle formed by drawing a horizontal line segment from point A to a vertical line segment from point B. Use this method to draw another right triangle, $\triangle DEF$, with its longest side on the line.

b. What can you conclude about the two triangles in part (a)? Justify your conclusion. Compare your results with other pairs.

c. Based on your conclusions in part (b), what is true about $\dfrac{BC}{AC}$ and the corresponding measure in $\triangle DEF$? What do these values tell you about the line?

4.2 **Notetaking with Vocabulary**

Vocabulary:

Notes:

4.2 **Self-Assessment**

Use the scale below to rate your understanding of the learning target and the success criteria.

1	2	3	4
I do not understand.	I can do it with help.	I can do it on my own.	I can teach someone else.

	Rating	Date
4.2 Slope of a Line		
Learning Target: Find and interpret the slope of a line.	1 2 3 4	
I can explain the meaning of slope.	1 2 3 4	
I can find the slope of a line.	1 2 3 4	
I can interpret the slope of a line in a real-life problem.	1 2 3 4	

4.2 Practice

Find the slope of the line.

1.

2.

The points in the table lie on a line. Find the slope of the line.

3.

x	0	2	4	6
y	-4	-1	2	5

4.

x	-4	-1	0	3
y	7	4	3	0

5. A ramp used to remove furniture from a moving truck has a slope of $\frac{2}{5}$. The height of the ramp is 4 feet. How far does the base of the ramp extend from the end of the truck?

6. The graph shows the cost of a data usage on a phone plan.

a. Find the slope of the line.

b. Explain the meaning of the slope as a rate of change.

c. How much money is added to the phone bill if you use 5 gigabytes of data?

d. How many gigabytes did you use if the data usage costs $30?

Use an equation to find the value of *k* so that the line that passes through the given points has the given slope. Explain your reasoning.

7. $(1, -1), (-2, k); m = -4$

8. $(-3, -4), (k, -2); m = \frac{2}{3}$

4.3 Graphing Proportional Relationships
For use with Exploration 4.3

Learning Target: Graph proportional relationships.

Success Criteria:
- I can graph an equation that represents a proportional relationship.
- I can write an equation that represents a proportional relationship.
- I can use graphs to compare proportional relationships.

---

1 **EXPLORATION:** Using a Ratio Table to Find Slope

Work with a partner. The graph shows amounts of vinegar and water that can be used to make a cleaning product.

a. Use the graph to make a ratio table relating the quantities. Explain how the slope of the line is represented in the table.

b. Make a ratio table that represents a different ratio of vinegar to water. Use the table to describe the slope of the graph of the new relationship.

4.3 **Graphing Proportional Relationships** (continued)

2 **EXPLORATION:** Deriving an Equation

Work with a partner. Let (x, y) represent any point on the graph of a proportional relationship.

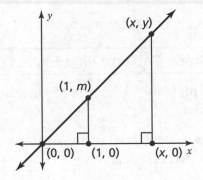

a. Describe the relationship between the corresponding side lengths of the triangles shown in the graph. Explain your reasoning.

b. Use the relationship in part (a) to write an equation relating y, m, and x. Then solve the equation for y.

c. What does your equation in part (b) describe? What does m represent? Explain your reasoning.

4.3 Notetaking with Vocabulary

Vocabulary:

Notes:

4.3 Self-Assessment

Use the scale below to rate your understanding of the learning target and the success criteria.

1	2	3	4
I do not understand.	I can do it with help.	I can do it on my own.	I can teach someone else.

	Rating	Date
4.3 Graphing Proportional Relationships		
Learning Target: Graph proportional relationships.	1 2 3 4	
I can graph an equation that represents a proportional relationship.	1 2 3 4	
I can write an equation that represents a proportional relationship.	1 2 3 4	
I can use graphs to compare proportional relationships.	1 2 3 4	

Name _____ Date _____

Tell whether x and y are in a proportional relationship. Explain your reasoning. If so, write an equation that represents the relationship.

1.

2.

3.

x	2	5	8	11
y	8	20	32	44

4.

x	3	6	9	12
y	2	4	6	8

5. The cost y (in dollars) to rent a lane at bowling alley A is proportional to the number x of hours that you rent the lane. It costs $18 to rent the lane for 2 hours.

   a. Write an equation that represents the situation.

   b. Interpret the slope of the graph of the equation.

   c. How much does it cost to rent the lane for 3 hours?

   d. At bowling alley B it costs $16.50 to rent a lane for 2 hours. Write an equation that represents the situation.

   e. In the same coordinate plane, graph equations that represent the costs of renting a lane for 2 hours at bowling alley A and bowling alley B. Compare and interpret the steepness of each graph.

6. The graph relates the height of the water in a tank y (in inches) to the volume of the water x (in gallons).

   a. Is the relationship proportional? Explain.

   b. Write an equation of the line. Interpret the slope.

   c. What is the height of the water in the tank when the volume is 250 gallons?

4.4 Graphing Linear Equations in Slope-Intercept Form
For use with Exploration 4.4

Learning Target: Graph linear equations in slope-intercept form.

Success Criteria:
- I can identify the slope and *y*-intercept of a line given an equation.
- I can rewrite a linear equation in slope-intercept form.
- I can use the slope and *y*-intercept to graph linear equations.

1 EXPLORATION: Deriving an Equation

Work with a partner. In the previous section, you learned that the graph of a proportional relationship can be represented by the equation $y = mx$, where m is the constant of proportionality.

a. You translate the graph of a proportional relationship 3 units up as shown below. Let (x, y) represent any point on the graph. Make a conjecture about the equation of the line. Explain your reasoning.

4.4 **Graphing Linear Equations in Slope-Intercept Form** (continued)

b. Describe the relationship between the corresponding side lengths of the triangles. Explain your reasoning.

c. Use the relationship in part (b) to write an equation relating y, m, and x. Does your equation support your conjecture in part (a)? Explain.

d. You translate the graph of a proportional relationship b units up. Write an equation relating y, m, x, and b. Justify your answer.

Name_____ Date_____

 Notetaking with Vocabulary

Vocabulary:

Notes:

 Self-Assessment

Use the scale below to rate your understanding of the learning target and the success criteria.

1	**2**	**3**	**4**
I do not understand.	I can do it with help.	I can do it on my own.	I can teach someone else.

	Rating	Date
4.4 Graphing Linear Equations in Slope-Intercept Form		
Learning Target: Graph linear equations in slope-intercept form.	1 2 3 4	
I can identify the slope and y-intercept of a line given an equation.	1 2 3 4	
I can rewrite a linear equation in slope-intercept form.	1 2 3 4	
I can use the slope and y-intercept to graph linear equations.	1 2 3 4	

4.4 Practice

Find the slope and the *y*-intercept of the graph of the linear equation.

1. $y = -\dfrac{3}{8}x + 10$

2. $y + \dfrac{1}{5} = -\dfrac{4}{5}x$

3. The number y of gallons of water in the swimming pool x minutes after turning on the faucet is represented by $y = 24x + 285$.

   a. Graph the linear equation.

   b. Interpret the slope and the y-intercept.

   c. Is the x-intercept applicable to the problem? Explain.

Graph the linear equation. Identify the *x*-intercept.

4. $y = -1.2x + 9$

5. $y + 3 = -\dfrac{6}{7}x$

6. There is a $10 monthly membership fee to download music. There is a $0.50 fee for each song downloaded.

   a. Write a linear equation that models the cost of downloading x songs per month.

   b. Graph the equation.

   c. What is the cost of downloading 15 songs? Explain your reasoning.

7. An entrepreneur is opening a business to market pies and pie fillings based on her family's recipes. The price of every item in the store is $6.

   a. Write a linear equation that models the amount of revenue y (in dollars) taken in for selling x items.

   b. Graph the equation.

   c. The monthly cost of rent and utilities for the store space is $1100. What is the minimum number of items that must be sold each month in order to make a profit? Explain your reasoning.

   d. Assuming 4 weeks in a month, what is the average number of items that need to be sold each week in order to turn a profit?

4.5 Graphing Linear Equations in Standard Form
For use with Exploration 4.5

Learning Target: Graph linear equations in standard form.

Success Criteria:
- I can rewrite the standard form of a linear equation in slope-intercept form.
- I can find intercepts of linear equations written in standard form.
- I can use intercepts to graph linear equations.

---

1 EXPLORATION: Using Intercepts

Work with a partner. You spend $150 on fruit trays and vegetable trays for a party.

Fruit Tray: $50   **Vegetable Tray: $25**

a. You buy x fruit trays and y vegetable trays. Complete the verbal model. Then use the verbal model to write an equation that relates x and y.

$$\frac{\overline{\hspace{1cm}}}{1 \text{ fruit tray}} \cdot \begin{array}{c}\text{Number} \\ \text{of fruit} \\ \text{trays}\end{array} + \frac{\overline{\hspace{1cm}}}{1 \text{ vegetable tray}} \cdot \begin{array}{c}\text{Number} \\ \text{of vegetable} \\ \text{trays}\end{array} = \underline{\hspace{1cm}}$$

b. What is the greatest number of fruit trays that you can buy? vegetable trays? Can you use these numbers to graph your equation from part (a) in the coordinate plane? Explain.

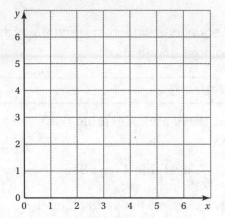

c. Use a graph to determine the different combinations of fruit trays and vegetable trays that you can buy. Justify your answers algebraically.

d. You are given an extra $50 to spend. How does this affect the intercepts of your graph in part (c)? Explain your reasoning?

4.5 Notetaking with Vocabulary

Vocabulary:

Notes:

4.5 Self-Assessment

Use the scale below to rate your understanding of the learning target and the success criteria.

1	**2**	**3**	**4**
I do not understand.	I can do it with help.	I can do it on my own.	I can teach someone else.

	Rating	Date
4.5 Graphing Linear Equations in Standard Form		
Learning Target: Graph linear equations in standard form.	1 2 3 4	
I can rewrite the standard form of a linear equation in slope-intercept form.	1 2 3 4	
I can find intercepts of linear equations written in standard form.	1 2 3 4	
I can use intercepts to graph linear equations.	1 2 3 4	

4.5 Practice

Write the linear equation in slope-intercept form.

1. $\frac{2}{3}x + y = 4$

2. $4x - 2y = 10$

Graph the linear equation.

3. $4.5x - 0.5y = 3$

4. $\frac{2}{3}x + \frac{1}{3}y = 2$

5. You work at the local pool as a lifeguard and you also work in the snack bar. You earn $15 per hour lifeguarding and $8 per hour working in the snack bar. Last week you worked a total of 20 hours and earned $202.

   a. Write an equation in standard form for the hours you worked.

   b. Write an equation in standard form for the money you earned.

   c. Graph both equations on the same coordinate plane.

   d. Determine how many hours you worked as a lifeguard and how many hours you worked in the snack bar. Explain your reasoning.

Graph the linear equation using intercepts.

6. $\frac{1}{5}x + \frac{1}{10}y = \frac{2}{5}$

7. $2.5x - 1.25y = 5$

8. Your family is on a ski vacation. Lift tickets for the family cost $80 per day. Snowboard rentals cost $40 per day. You purchase lift tickets for x days and snowboard rentals for y days and spend $480.

   a. Write an equation in standard form that represents the situation.

   b. Find the x- and y-intercepts.

   c. Graph the equation.

   d. You rent snowboards for 2 days. How many days did you purchase lift tickets?

9. An electrician charges $80 plus $32 per hour.

   a. Write an equation that represents the total fee y (in dollars) charged by the electrician for a job lasting x hours.

   b. Find the x- and y-intercepts.

   c. Graph the equation.

   d. Is the value of the x-intercept applicable to the electrician? Explain.

4.6 Writing Equations in Slope-Intercept Form
For use with Exploration 4.6

Learning Target: Write equations of lines in slope-intercept form.

Success Criteria:
- I can find the slope and the *y*-intercept of a line.
- I can use the slope and the *y*-intercept to write an equation of a line.
- I can write equations in slope-intercept form to solve real-life problems.

---

1 EXPLORATION: Writing Equations of Lines

Work with a partner. For each part, answer the following questions.

- **What are the slopes and the *y*-intercepts of the lines?**

- **What are equations that represent the lines?**

- **What do the lines have in common?**

a.

b.
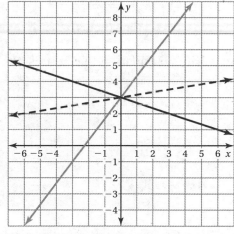

4.6 **Writing Equations in Slope-Intercept Form** (continued)

---

2 **EXPLORATION:** Interpreting the Slope and the *y*-intercept

Work with a partner. The graph represents the distance *y* (in miles) of a car from Phoenix after *t* hours of a trip.

a. Find the slope and the *y*-intercept of the line. What do they represent in this situation?

b. Write an equation that represents the graph.

c. How can you determine the distance of the car from Phoenix after 11 hours?

Name_____ Date_____

 Notetaking with Vocabulary

Vocabulary:

Notes:

4.6 **Self-Assessment**

Use the scale below to rate your understanding of the learning target and the success criteria.

1	*2*	*3*	*4*
I do not understand.	I can do it with help.	I can do it on my own.	I can teach someone else.

	Rating	Date
4.6 Writing Equations in Slope-Intercept Form		
Learning Target: Write equations of lines in slope-intercept form.	1 2 3 4	
I can find the slope and the y-intercept of a line.	1 2 3 4	
I can use the slope and the y-intercept to write an equation of a line.	1 2 3 4	
I can write equations in slope-intercept form to solve real-life problems.	1 2 3 4	

4.6 Practice

1. Write an equation that represents each side of the figure.

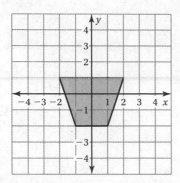

Write an equation in slope-intercept form of the line that passes through the given points.

2.

3.

4. Your hair is 6 inches long and grows at a rate of 144 millimeters per year.

   a. Convert 144 millimeters per year to inches per year. Round your answer to the nearest tenth.

   b. Write an equation that represents the length y (in inches) of your hair after x years.

   c. If you do not cut it, how long is your hair after 4 years?

Write an equation of the line that passes through the given points.

5. $(-4, -1), (0, 5)$

6. $(0, -3), (1, -5)$

7. Yesterday, you typed 8 pages in 48 minutes. Today, you typed 20 pages in 2 hours.

   a. Plot the two points (x, y), where x is the time (in minutes) and y is the number of pages.

   b. What is the rate of typing? Explain.

   c. Write an equation that represents the number of pages in terms of the number of minutes.

4.7 Writing Equations in Point-Slope Form
For use with Exploration 4.7

Learning Target: Write equations of lines in point-slope form.

Success Criteria:
- I can use a point on a line and the slope to write an equation of the line.
- I can use any two points to write an equation of a line.
- I can write equations in point-slope form to solve real-life problems.

---

1 EXPLORATION: Deriving an Equation

Work with a partner. Let (x_1, y_1) represent a specific point on a line. Let (x, y) represent any other point on the line.

a. Write an equation that represents the slope m of the line. Explain your reasoning.

b. Multiply each side of your equation in part (a) by the expression in the denominator. What does the resulting equation represent? Explain your reasoning.

4.7 Writing Equations in Point-Slope Form (continued)

2 EXPLORATION: Writing an Equation

Work with a partner.

For 4 months, you saved $25 a month. You now have $175 in your savings account.

a. Draw a graph that shows the balance in your account after t months.

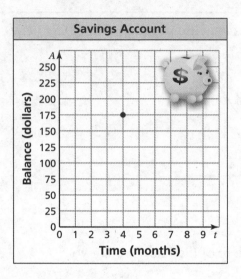

b. Use your result from Exploration 1 to write an equation that represents the balance A after t months.

Name_____ Date_____

4.7 Notetaking with Vocabulary

Vocabulary:

Notes:

4.7 Self-Assessment

Use the scale below to rate your understanding of the learning target and the success criteria.

1	2	3	4
I do not understand.	I can do it with help.	I can do it on my own.	I can teach someone else.

	Rating	Date
4.7 Writing Equations in Point-Slope Form		
Learning Target: Write equations of lines in point-slope form	1 2 3 4	
I can use a point on a line and the slope to write an equation of the line.	1 2 3 4	
I can use any two points to write an equation of a line.	1 2 3 4	
I can write equations in point-slope form to solve real-life problems.	1 2 3 4	

Name _____   Date _____

4.7 Practice

Write an equation of the line with the given slope that passes through the given point. Graph the line.

1. $m = \dfrac{5}{4}$

2. $m = -4$

Write an equation in point-slope form of the line that passes through the given point and has the given slope.

3. $(-6, 3); m = \dfrac{1}{3}$

4. $(8, -7); m = -\dfrac{3}{4}$

Write an equation in slope-intercept form of the line that passes through the given points.

5. $(2, 3), (3, 7)$

6. $(-5, -8), (10, 4)$

7. The cost of renting the party room for 10 people is $117.50. The cost of renting the room is $151.25 for 15 people. Write an equation that represents the cost of renting the party room in terms of the number of people attending the party.

8. You are pulling a kite back to the ground at a rate of 2 feet per second. After 4 seconds, the kite is 16 feet above the ground.

   a. Write an equation that represents the height y (in feet) of the kite above the ground after x seconds.

   b. At what height was the kite when you started pulling it in?

   c. When does the kite touch the ground?

9. Write an equation of the line that passes through the point (-12, 6) and is parallel to the graph of the equation $y = -\dfrac{1}{6}x + 1$. Explain your reasoning.

Name_____ Date _____

Use the scale below to rate your understanding of the learning target and the success criteria.

1	**2**	**3**	**4**
I do not understand.	I can do it with help.	I can do it on my own.	I can teach someone else.

	Rating	Date
4.1 Graphing Linear Equations		
Learning Target: Graph linear equations.	1 2 3 4	
I can create a table of values and write ordered pairs given a linear equation.	1 2 3 4	
I can plot ordered pairs to create a graph of a linear equation.	1 2 3 4	
I can use a graph of a linear equation to solve a real-life problem.	1 2 3 4	
4.2 Slope of a Line		
Learning Target: Find and interpret the slope of a line.	1 2 3 4	
I can explain the meaning of slope.	1 2 3 4	
I can find the slope of a line.	1 2 3 4	
I can interpret the slope of a line in a real-life problem.	1 2 3 4	
4.3 Graphing Proportional Relationships		
Learning Target: Graph proportional relationships.	1 2 3 4	
I can graph an equation that represents a proportional relationship.	1 2 3 4	
I can write an equation that represents a proportional relationship.	1 2 3 4	
I can use graphs to compare proportional relationships.	1 2 3 4	

Chapter 4

Chapter Self-Assessment (continued)

	Rating	Date
4.4 Graphing Linear Equations in Slope-Intercept Form		
Learning Target: Graph linear equations in slope-intercept form.	1 2 3 4	
I can identify the slope and y-intercept of a line given an equation.	1 2 3 4	
I can rewrite a linear equation in slope-intercept form.	1 2 3 4	
I can use the slope and y-intercept to graph linear equations.	1 2 3 4	
4.5 Graphing Linear Equations in Standard Form		
Learning Target: Graph linear equations in standard form.	1 2 3 4	
I can rewrite the standard form of a linear equation in slope-intercept form.	1 2 3 4	
I can find intercepts of linear equations written in standard form.	1 2 3 4	
I can use intercepts to graph linear equations.	1 2 3 4	
4.6 Writing Equations in Slope-Intercept Form		
Learning Target: Write equations of lines in slope-intercept form.	1 2 3 4	
I can find the slope and the y-intercept of a line.	1 2 3 4	
I can use the slope and the y-intercept to write an equation of a line.	1 2 3 4	
I can write equations in slope-intercept form to solve real-life problems.	1 2 3 4	
4.7 Writing Equations in Point-Slope Form		
Learning Target: Write equations of lines in point-slope form.	1 2 3 4	
I can use a point on a line and the slope to write an equation of the line.	1 2 3 4	
I can use any two points to write an equation of a line.	1 2 3 4	
I can write equations in point-slope form to solve real-life problems.	1 2 3 4	

Chapter 5 **Review & Refresh**

Simplify the expression.

1. $2x + 5 - x$

2. $4 + 2d - 4d$

3. $7y - 8 + 6y - 3$

4. $5 + 4z - 3 + 3z$

5. $4s + 2 + s - 1$

6. $24x - 5 - 3$

7. The width of a garden is $(4x - 1)$ feet and the length is $2x$ feet. Find the perimeter of the garden.

Chapter 5 Review & Refresh (continued)

Solve the equation. Check your solution.

8. $8y - 3 = 13$

9. $4a + 11 - a = 2$

10. $9 = 43k - 4 - 7k$

11. $-12 - 56 - 2m = 18$

12. $15 - t + 8t = -13$

13. $5h - 2\left(\frac{3}{2}h + 4\right) = 10$

14. The profit P (in dollars) from selling x calculators is $P = 25x - 10x + 250$. How many calculators are sold when the profit is $430?

Name_____ Date _____

5.1 Solving Systems of Linear Equations by Graphing
For use with Exploration 5.1

Learning Target: Understand how to solve systems of linear equations by graphing.

Success Criteria:
- I can graph a linear equation.
- I can find the point where two lines intersect.
- I can solve a system of linear equations by graphing.

---

1 EXPLORATION: Using a Graph to Solve a Problem

Work with a partner. You charge your headphones and your phone. The equations below represent the battery powers $p\%$ of the devices after x minutes of charging.

$$p = \frac{5}{3}x \qquad \text{Headphones}$$

$$p = x + 25 \qquad \text{Phone}$$

a. You check the battery power of each device every 10 minutes. Complete the table. How do the device's battery powers compare?

x (minutes)	10	20	30	40	50	60
p (headphones)						
p (phone)						

b. After how much time do the devices have the same battery power? What is the battery power at that time? Justify your answer.

c. The solutions of a linear equation are all the points on its graph. How many solutions can two linear equations share? Explain your reasoning.

d. Graph the battery power equations in the same coordinate plane. What do you notice?

e. Use a graphing calculator to check your answers in part (b). Explain your method.

Name_____ Date_____

5.1 Notetaking with Vocabulary

Vocabulary:

Notes:

5.1 Self-Assessment

Use the scale below to rate your understanding of the learning target and the success criteria.

1	**2**	**3**	**4**
I do not understand.	I can do it with help.	I can do it on my own.	I can teach someone else.

	Rating	Date
5.1 Solving Systems of Linear Equations by Graphing		
Learning Target: Understand how to solve systems of linear equations by graphing.	1 2 3 4	
I can graph a linear equation.	1 2 3 4	
I can find the point where two lines intersect.	1 2 3 4	
I can solve a system of linear equations by graphing.	1 2 3 4	

5.1 Practice

Solve the system of linear equations by graphing.

1. $x + y = 18$
$y = x + 12$

2. $y = 6x - 1$
$x - y = 11$

3. $y + x = 6$
$y = -1.5x + 10$

4. The cost C (in dollars) to rent the convention hall is $C = 10x + 1500$, where x is the number of admission tickets. Admission tickets to the convention are $16 each.

   a. Write an equation for the revenue R in terms of the number of admission tickets.

   b. How many admission tickets need to be sold in order for the convention to break even?

Use a graphing calculator to solve the system.

5. $x + 1.2y = 12.4$
$-1.5x + 2y = 8$

6. $3.4x + 1.5y = 0.4$
$3x - 2.4y = 7.8$

7. $-1.2x + 3.3y = 3.6$
$2.5x - 4y = -7.5$

8. A building has a total of 60 one-bedroom and two-bedroom apartments. There are twice as many one-bedroom apartments as two-bedroom apartments. How many apartments of each type are in the building? Use a system of linear equations to justify your answer.

9. Is it possible for a system of two linear equations to have no solution? Explain your reasoning.

10. The hare challenged the tortoise to a race from the water fountain to the park bench. In order to ensure a fair race, the tortoise will start 100 feet in front of the hare. The tortoise is walking at a rate of 2 feet per minute. The hare is walking at a rate of 6 feet per minute.

   a. How long will it take for the hare to catch up to the tortoise?

   b. How long did the hare wait before walking (in order for the tortoise to walk 100 feet)?

   c. The distance from the water fountain to the park bench is 130 feet. Who won the race?

Name_____ Date_____

5.2 Solving Systems of Linear Equations by Substitution
For use with Exploration 5.2

Learning Target: Understand how to solve systems of linear equations by substitution.

Success Criteria:
- I can solve a linear equation in two variables for either variable.
- I can solve a system of linear equations by substitution.

1 EXPLORATION: Solving Systems Algebraically

Work with a partner.

a. Find the value of each symbol in the systems below. Compare your solution methods with other pairs of students.

System 1:
$$☽ + ☽ - 1 = ★ \quad \text{Equation 1}$$
$$☽ + ★ + ★ = 8 \quad \text{Equation 2}$$

System 2:
$$✿ - ❋ = 3 \quad \text{Equation 1}$$
$$✿ + ❋ = 1 \quad \text{Equation 2}$$

b. Use a method similar to your method in part (a) to solve the system below. Then explain how to solve a system of linear equations in two variables algebraically.

$$3x + y = 1 \qquad \text{Equation 1}$$

$$x - y = -5 \qquad \text{Equation 2}$$

5.2   **Solving Systems of Linear Equations by Substitution** (continued)

---

2 **EXPLORATION:** Writing and Solving Systems of Equations

Work with a partner. Roll two number cubes that are different colors. Then write the ordered pair shown by the number cubes.

    a. Write a system of linear equations that has your ordered pair as its solution. Explain how you found your system.

    b. Exchange systems with another pair of students. Use a method from Exploration 1 to solve the system.

5.2 Notetaking with Vocabulary

Vocabulary:

Notes:

5.2 Self-Assessment

Use the scale below to rate your understanding of the learning target and the success criteria.

1	*2*	*3*	*4*
I do not understand.	I can do it with help.	I can do it on my own.	I can teach someone else.

	Rating	Date
5.2 Solving Systems of Linear Equations by Substitution		
Learning Target: Understand how to solve systems of linear equations by substitution.	1 2 3 4	
I can solve a linear equation in two variables for either variable.	1 2 3 4	
I can solve a system of linear equations by substitution.	1 2 3 4	

Big Ideas Math: Modeling Real Life Grade 7 Advanced **113**
Student Journal

5.2 Practice

Solve the system by substitution. Check your solution.

1. $x + 4y = -1$
   $-3x - 14 = y$

2. $3y = -2x$
   $y = x - 5$

3. $\frac{1}{2}x + 2y = 3$
   $6y + 1 = x$

4. The revenue for a vehicle rental store is $5460. There were 208 cars and 52 vans rented. A van rents for $10 more than a car.

   a. Write a system of equations that represents this situation.

   b. What is the cost of the car rental?

   c. What is the cost of the van rental?

Solve the system by substitution. Explain which variable you solved for and why you chose that variable.

5. $2x - y = 6$
   $x = y - 1$

6. $2x + 4y = -4$
   $x - 3y = -12$

7. $4x + 2y = 8$
   $6x - 4y = 5$

8. The sum of the digits of a two-digit number is 11. The tens digit is one less than three times the ones digit. Find the original number.

9. The farmers' market has a total of 98 tents. The ratio of food tents to retail tents is 9 : 5.

   a. Write a system of linear equations that represents this situation.

   b. How many food tents are at the farmers' market?

   c. How many retail tents are at the farmers' market?

10. Forty-five children attend a preschool. The number of two-year-olds is one half the number of three-year-olds. The number of four-year-olds is the same as the number of three-year-olds.

   a. How many two-year-olds attend the preschool?

   b. How many three-year-olds attend the preschool?

   c. How many four-year-olds attend the preschool?

5.3 Solving Systems of Linear Equations by Elimination
For use with Exploration 5.3

Learning Target: Understand how to solve systems of linear equations by elimination.

Success Criteria:
- I can add or subtract equations in a system.
- I can use the Multiplication Property of Equality to produce equivalent equations.
- I can solve a system of linear equations by elimination.

1 EXPLORATION: Solving Systems Algebraically

Work with a partner. A student found the value of x in the system using substitution as shown.

$$3x + y = 1 \qquad \text{Equation 1}$$
$$x - y = -5 \qquad \text{Equation 2}$$

| Step 1: | $3x + y = 1$ | Equation 1 |
| | $x + 5 = y$ | Revised Equation 2 |

Step 2:	$3x + x + 5 = 1$	Substitute $x + 5$ for y in Equation 1.
	$4x + 5 = 1$	Combine like terms.
	$4x = -4$	Subtract 5 from each side.
	$x = -1$	Divide each side by 4.

a. Find another way to obtain the equation $4x = -4$ from the original system. Does your method produce an equation in one variable for any system? Explain.

5.3 **Solving Systems of Linear Equations by Elimination** (continued)

b. Can you use your method in part (a) to solve each system below? If so, solve the system. If not, replace one of the equations with an equivalent equation that allow you to use your method in part (a). Then solve the system.

System 1:
$$2x + 3y = -4 \qquad \text{Equation 1}$$
$$2x - 3y = 8 \qquad \text{Equation 2}$$

System 2:
$$x + 4y = -5 \qquad \text{Equation 1}$$
$$3x - 2y = 13 \qquad \text{Equation 2}$$

c. Compare your solution methods in part (b) with other pairs of students.

Name_____ Date_____

 Notetaking with Vocabulary

Vocabulary:

Notes:

5.3 **Self-Assessment**

Use the scale below to rate your understanding of the learning target and the success criteria.

1	**2**	**3**	**4**
I do not understand.	I can do it with help.	I can do it on my own.	I can teach someone else.

	Rating	Date
5.3 Solving Systems of Linear Equations by Elimination		
Learning Target: Understand how to solve systems of linear equations by elimination.	1 2 3 4	
I can add or subtract equations in a system.	1 2 3 4	
I can use the Multiplication Property of Equality to produce equivalent equations.	1 2 3 4	
I can solve a system of linear equations by elimination.	1 2 3 4	

5.3 Practice

Solve the system by elimination. Check your solution.

1. $3x - y = 0$
$-3x + 5y = 0$

2. $2x - 4y = -2$
$2x + 3y = -16$

3. $x + 3y = 17$
$-2x + 3y = -7$

4. You and your friend are selling magazine subscriptions. You sell 8 fewer magazine subscriptions than your friend. Together you sell 42 magazine subscriptions.

    a. Write a system of linear equations that represents this situation.

    b. How many magazine subscriptions did you sell?

    c. How many magazine subscriptions did your friend sell?

Solve the system by elimination. Explain your reasoning for choosing which variable to eliminate.

5. $2x + 5y = -3$
$3x - y = 21$

6. $2y = -5x - 3$
$4x - 2 = -6y$

7. $3y = x - 6$
$2x = 3y + 3$

8. For what value(s) of a and b might you solve the system by elimination?

    a. $3x + 5y = 10$
       $2x + ay = 4$

    b. $-4x - 3y = 9$
       $bx + 7y = 2$

9. Your friend rents 10 chairs and 2 tables for \$300. Another friend rents 8 chairs and 4 tables for \$360. You want to rent 12 chairs and 3 tables. How much do you expect to pay?

10. One equation in a system of line equations is $x - 3y = 1$. The solution of the system of linear equations is $(4, 1)$.

    a. Find the value of a such that the equation $2x + ay = 5$ is the second equation in the system.

    b. Find the value of b such that the equation $bx + 5y = 1$ is the second equation in the system.

    c. Find the value of c such that the equation $2x - 7y = c$ is the second equation in the system.

11. Write a system of linear equations that contains $3x - y = 0$ and has a solution $(-2, -6)$.

5.4 Solving Special Systems of Linear Equations
For use with Exploration 5.4

Learning Target: Solve systems with different numbers of solutions.

Success Criteria:
- I can determine the number of solutions of a system.
- I can solve a system of linear equations with any number of solutions.

1 EXPLORATION: Exploring Solutions of Systems

Work with a partner. You spend $50 on a sewing machine to make dog backpacks. Each backpack costs you $15 for materials.

a. Represent the cost y (in dollars) to make x backpacks in the coordinate plane.

b. You charge $25 per backpack. How many backpacks do you have to sell to *break even*? Use a graph to justify your answer.

5.4 Solving Special Systems of Linear Equations (continued)

c. Can you break even when you sell each backpack for $20? $15? Use graphs to justify your answers.

d. Explain whether it is possible for a system of linear equations to have the numbers of solutions below.

- no solution

- exactly one solution

- exactly two solutions

- infinitely many solutions

Name_____ Date_____

 5.4 **Notetaking with Vocabulary**

Vocabulary:

Notes:

5.4 **Self-Assessment**

Use the scale below to rate your understanding of the learning target and
the success criteria.

1	*2*	*3*	*4*
I do not understand.	I can do it with help.	I can do it on my own.	I can teach someone else.

	Rating	Date
5.4 Solving Special Systems of Linear Equations		
Learning Target: Solve systems with different numbers of solutions.	1 2 3 4	
I can determine the number of solutions of a system.	1 2 3 4	
I can solve a system of linear equations with any number of solutions.	1 2 3 4	

5.4 Practice

Solve the system of linear equations. Explain your choice of method.

1. $y = \frac{1}{4}x - 1$

   $y = \frac{1}{4}x + 5$

2. $y = -2x - 1$

   $5x + 2y = -5$

3. $3\left(x - \frac{2}{3}y\right) = 4$

   $3x + 5 = 2y$

4. $\pi x - 2y = 2\pi$

   $y = \frac{\pi}{2}x - \pi$

5. $x = 2y$

   $6y + 3x = 0$

6. $4x + 3y = 10$

   $2x + \frac{3}{2}y = 5$

7. y is 6 less than 3 times x. x is 2 more than one-third of y. Find the solution of the puzzle.

8. Both equations in a system of linear equations have a slope of $\frac{1}{2}$. Does this system have infinitely many solutions? Explain.

9. You and a friend go to a farmers' market. You spend $13 on fruit. Then you and your friend each buy the same number of tomato plants for $4 each.

   a. Write a system of linear equations that represents this situation.

   b. Will you and your friend spend the same amount of money? Explain.

10. Write a system of linear equations that has infinitely many solutions.

11. Write a system of linear equations that has the solution $(2, 1)$.

12. Write a system of linear equations that has no solution.

13. Find the values of a and b so the system shown has no solution.

    $5x = 2y + 1$
    $ax = 6y + b$

14. One equation in a system of linear equations has a slope of $\frac{2}{5}$. The other equation has a slope of $-\frac{5}{2}$.

    a. How many solutions does the system have? Explain.

    b. Without graphing, determine if the graphs of the two equations are *parallel, perpendicular, or neither*.

Chapter Self-Assessment

Use the scale below to rate your understanding of the learning target and the success criteria.

1	2	3	4
I do not understand.	I can do it with help.	I can do it on my own.	I can teach someone else.

	Rating	Date
5.1 Solving Systems of Linear Equations by Graphing		
Learning Target: Understand how to solve systems of linear equations by graphing.	1 2 3 4	
I can graph a linear equation.	1 2 3 4	
I can find the point where two lines intersect.	1 2 3 4	
I can solve a system of linear equations by graphing.	1 2 3 4	
5.2 Solving Systems of Linear Equations by Substitution		
Learning Target: Understand how to solve systems of linear equations by substitution.	1 2 3 4	
I can solve a linear equation in two variables for either variable.	1 2 3 4	
I can solve a system of linear equations by substitution.	1 2 3 4	
5.3 Solving Systems of Linear Equations by Elimination		
Learning Target: Understand how to solve systems of linear equations by elimination.	1 2 3 4	
I can add or subtract equations in a system.	1 2 3 4	
I can use the Multiplication Property of Equality to produce equivalent equations.	1 2 3 4	
I can solve a system of linear equations by elimination.	1 2 3 4	

Chapter Self-Assessment (continued)

	Rating	Date
5.4 Solving Special Systems of Linear Equations		
Learning Target: Solve systems with different numbers of solutions.	1 2 3 4	
I can determine the number of solutions of a system.	1 2 3 4	
I can solve a system of linear equations with any number of solutions.	1 2 3 4	

Chapter 6 Review & Refresh

Plot the ordered pair in a coordinate plane. Describe the location of the point.

1. $(2, 1)$

2. $(-3, 3)$

3. $(4, -2)$

4. $(-1, -1)$

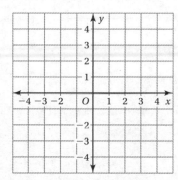

5. Describe the location of the vertices of the triangle.

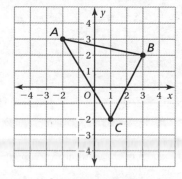

Chapter 6 **Review & Refresh** (continued)

Write in slope-intercept form an equation of the line that passes through the given points.

6. $(-2, -2), (1, 7)$

7. $(5, -1), (-5, 11)$

8. $(-20, -8), (5, 12)$

9. $(6, -11), (-3, 1)$

10. $(-1, -3), (2, 6)$

11. $(-3, 6), (4, -8)$

6.1 Scatter Plots
For use with Exploration 6.1

Learning Target: Use scatter plots to describe patterns and relationships between two quantities.

Success Criteria:
- I can make a scatter plot.
- I can identify outliers, gaps, and clusters in a scatter plot.
- I can use scatter plots to describe relationships between data.

---

1 EXPLORATION: Finding Relationships Between Data

Work with a partner. The weights and circumferences of several sports balls are shown.

Sports Ball	Weight (oz)	Circumference (in.)
Basketball	21	30
Baseball	5	9
Golf	1.6	5.3
Soccer	16	28
Tennis	2	8
Racquetball	1.4	7
Water Polo	15	27
Softball	7	12
Volleyball	10	26

a. Represent the data in the coordinate plane. Explain your method.

6.1 **Scatter Plots** (continued)

b. Is there a relationship between the size and the weight of a sports ball?
Explain your reasoning.

c. Is it reasonable to use the graph to predict the weights of the sports balls
below? Explain your reasoning.

- **Kickball:** circumference = 26 in.

- **Bowling ball:** circumference = 27 in.

Notetaking with Vocabulary

Vocabulary:

Notes:

6.1 **Self-Assessment**

Use the scale below to rate your understanding of the learning target and the success criteria.

1	**2**	**3**	**4**
I do not understand.	I can do it with help.	I can do it on my own.	I can teach someone else.

	Rating	Date
6.1 Scatter Plots		
Learning Target: Use scatter plots to describe patterns and relationships between two quantities.	1 2 3 4	
I can make a scatter plot.	1 2 3 4	
I can identify outliers, gaps, and clusters in a scatter plot.	1 2 3 4	
I can use scatter plots to describe relationships between data.	1 2 3 4	

Big Ideas Math: Modeling Real Life Grade 7 Advanced **129**
Student Journal

Name _____ Date _____

1. The table shows the numbers of students remaining on an after-school bus and the numbers of minutes since leaving the school.

Number of students	56	45	39	24	17	6	0
Minutes	0	5	9	15	23	26	32

   a. Write the ordered pairs from the table and plot them in a coordinate plane.

   b. Describe the relationship between the two data sets.

2. The scatter plot shows the numbers of bushels filled and the numbers of apples picked.

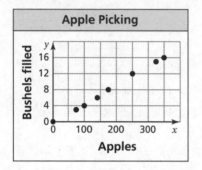

   a. How many bushels are needed for 350 apples?

   b. About how many apples can be placed in 8 bushels?

   c. Describe the relationship shown by the data.

3. Describe a set of real-life data that has a positive linear relationship.

4. The scatter plot shows the numbers of yard sales in your neighborhood each month for a year.

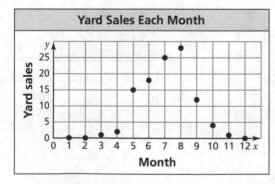

   a. How many yard sales are during the month of February? June?

   b. During which month(s) are there no yard sales?

   c. What type of relationship do the data show?

   d. What type of climate might this neighborhood have?

   e. Identify any outliers, gaps, or clusters and explain why they might exist.

Name_____ Date_____

6.2 Lines of Fit
For use with Exploration 6.2

Learning Target: Use lines of fit to model data.

Success Criteria:
- I can write and interpret an equation of a line of fit.
- I can find an equation of a line of best fit.
- I can use a line of fit to make predictions.

---

1 **EXPLORATION:** Representing Data by a Linear Equation

Work with a partner. You have been working on a science project for 8 months. Each month, you measured the length of a baby alligator.

The table shows your measurements.

	September							April
Month, x	0	1	2	3	4	5	6	7
Length (in.), y	22.0	22.5	23.5	25.0	26.0	27.5	28.5	29.5

a. Use a scatter plot to draw a line that you think best describes the relationship between the data.

6.2 **Lines of Fit** (continued)

b. Write an equation for your line in part (a).

c. Use your equation in part (b) to predict the length of the baby alligator next September.

6.2 Notetaking with Vocabulary

Vocabulary:

Notes:

6.2 Self-Assessment

Use the scale below to rate your understanding of the learning target and the success criteria.

1	2	3	4
I do not understand.	I can do it with help.	I can do it on my own.	I can teach someone else.

	Rating	Date
6.2 Lines of Fit		
Learning Target: Use lines of fit to model data.	1 2 3 4	
I can write and interpret an equation of a line of fit.	1 2 3 4	
I can find an equation of a line of best fit.	1 2 3 4	
I can use a line of fit to make predictions.	1 2 3 4	

6.2 Practice

1. The table shows the costs (in dollars) of bottles of juice (in fluid ounces).

Juice (oz)	Cost ($)
12	$1.75
20	$3
32	$4
64	$6.50
128	$12

a. Make a scatter plot of the data and draw a line of best fit.

b. Write an equation of the line of best fit.

c. Interpret the slope and the y-intercept of the line of best fit.

d. Assuming this trend continues, what would be the cost of a 256-fluid ounce container of juice? Explain your reasoning.

e. Identify and interpret the correlation coefficient.

2. The table shows the mortgage interest rates y at a local bank for the years 2010 through 2017.

Year since 2010, x	0	1	2	3	4	5	6	7
Rate (%), y	4.7	4.4	3.6	3.9	4.1	3.8	3.6	3.9

a. Make a scatter plot of the data.

b. Draw a line of best fit.

c. Write an equation of the line of best fit.

d. Interpret the slope of the line of best fit.

e. Assuming this trend continues, what would be the mortgage interest rate for the year 2020? Explain your reasoning.

f. Identify and interpret the correlation coefficient.

3. Which correlation coefficient indicates a weaker relationship: −0.145 or 0.127? Explain.

6.3 Two-Way Tables

For use with Exploration 6.3

Learning Target: Use two-way tables to represent data.

Success Criteria:
- I can read a two-way table.
- I can make a two-way table.
- I can use a two-way table to describe relationships between data.

1 EXPLORATION: Analyzing Data

Work with a partner. You are the manager of a sports shop. The table shows the numbers of soccer T-shirts that your shop has left in stock at the end of a soccer season.

		T-Shirt Size					
		S	M	L	XL	XXL	Total
Color	Blue/White	5	4	1	0	2	
	Blue/Gold	3	6	5	2	0	
	Red/White	4	2	4	1	3	
	Black/White	3	4	1	2	1	
	Black/Gold	5	2	3	0	2	
	Total						65

a. Complete the table.

b. Are there any black-and-gold XL T-shirts in stock? Justify your answer.

6.3 **Two-Way Tables** (continued)

c. The numbers of T-shirts you ordered at the beginning of the soccer season
are shown below. Complete the table.

		T-Shirt Size					
		S	M	L	XL	XXL	Total
Color	Blue/White	5	6	7	6	5	
	Blue/Gold	5	6	7	6	5	
	Red/White	5	6	7	6	5	
	Black/White	5	6	7	6	5	
	Black/Gold	5	6	7	6	5	
	Total						

d. How would you alter the numbers of T-shirts you order for the next soccer
season?

Name_____ Date_____

 6.3 **Notetaking with Vocabulary**

Vocabulary:

Notes:

6.3 **Self-Assessment**

Use the scale below to rate your understanding of the learning target and the success criteria.

1	**2**	**3**	**4**
I do not understand.	I can do it with help.	I can do it on my own.	I can teach someone else.

	Rating	Date
6.3 Two-Way Tables		
Learning Target: Use two-way tables to represent data.	1 2 3 4	
I can read a two-way table.	1 2 3 4	
I can make a two-way table.	1 2 3 4	
I can use a two-way table to describe relationships between data.	1 2 3 4	

6.3 Practice

1. Find and interpret the marginal frequencies.

		Number of doors	
		Two	Four
Number of Cylinders	Four	54	25
	Six	37	84

2. You randomly survey students in your school. You ask whether they spend more leisure time watching television, playing video games, or going online. You display your results in the two-way table.

		Leisure Time		
		Television	Video Games	Internet
Grade	10th	25	38	12
	11th	32	26	16
	12th	30	20	30

   a. How many 11th-graders chose playing video games?

   b. Find and interpret the marginal frequencies for the survey.

   c. What percent of students in the survey are the 12th-graders who spend more time going online?

3. You randomly survey your classmates about the color of their hair. The results are shown in the tables.

Hair Color of Female Classmates

Red	Blonde	Brunette	Black
3	15	41	33

Hair Color of Male Classmates

Red	Blonde	Brunette	Black
4	21	30	27

   a. Make a two-way table.

   b. Find and interpret the marginal frequencies for the survey.

   c. For each hair color, what percent of the students in the survey are female? male? Organize the results in a two-way table.

6.4 Choosing a Data Display
For use with Exploration 6.4

Learning Target: Use appropriate data displays to represent situations.

Success Criteria:
- I can choose appropriate data displays for situations.
- I can identify misleading data displays.
- I can analyze a variety of data displays.

1 EXPLORATION: Displaying Data

Work with a partner. Analyze and display each data set in a way that best describes the data. Explain your choice of display.

a. A group of schools in New England participated in a two-month study. They reported 3962 dead animals.

Birds: 307   Mammals: 2746

Amphibians: 145   Reptiles: 75

Unknown: 689

6.4 Choosing a Data Display (continued)

b. The data below show the numbers of black bears killed on a state's roads each year for 20 years.

Year 1:	30	Year 8:	47	Year 15:	99
Year 2:	37	Year 9:	49	Year 16:	129
Year 3:	46	Year 10:	61	Year 17:	111
Year 4:	33	Year 11:	74	Year 18:	127
Year 5:	43	Year 12:	88	Year 19:	141
Year 6:	35	Year 13:	82	Year 20:	135
Year 7:	43	Year 14:	109		

c. A one-week study along a four-mile section of road found the following weights (in pounds) of raccoons that had been killed by vehicles.

13.4	14.8	17.0	12.9
21.3	21.5	16.8	14.8
15.2	18.7	18.6	17.2
18.5	9.4	19.4	15.7
14.5	9.5	25.4	21.5
17.3	19.1	11.0	12.4
20.4	13.6	17.5	18.5
21.5	14.0	13.9	19.0

d. What can be done to minimize the number of animals killed by vehicles?

Notetaking with Vocabulary

Vocabulary:

Notes:

6.4 **Self-Assessment**

Use the scale below to rate your understanding of the learning target and the success criteria.

1	*2*	*3*	*4*
I do not understand.	I can do it with help.	I can do it on my own.	I can teach someone else.

	Rating	Date
6.4 Choosing a Data Display		
Learning Target: Use appropriate data displays to represent situations.	1 2 3 4	
I can choose appropriate data displays for situations.	1 2 3 4	
I can identify misleading data displays.	1 2 3 4	
I can analyze a variety of data displays.	1 2 3 4	

Name _____ Date _____

6.4 Practice

Choose an appropriate data display for the situation. Explain your reasoning.

1. the heights of girls in grades 6 through 12

2. the numbers of computers offered within $100 price ranges

3. the comparison of the number of students and the number of office staff

4. the percentages of income budgeted for food, utilities, housing, gas, and education

Explain why the data set is misleading.

5.

6.

7. You spin a spinner 20 times and want to use a data display to show the number of times each of the numbers 1 through 5 occurs. Choose an appropriate data display for the situation. Explain your reasoning.

8. What type of data display is appropriate for showing the median of the data values?

9. A professor wants to use a data display to show the relationship between class sizes and passing rates for college students. Choose an appropriate data display for the situation. Explain your reasoning.

10. A dentist wants to use a data display to show the percentages of clients using different types of toothbrushes. Choose an appropriate data display for the situation. Explain your reasoning.

11. The new executive was making a presentation to the Board of Directors. He used a pictograph to show the weekly profits made by his department during the last 3 months.

    a. Explain why this would be an inappropriate use of a data display.

    b. Choose an appropriate data display for his situation.

Name_____ Date_____

Chapter Self-Assessment

Use the scale below to rate your understanding of the learning target and the success criteria.

1	**2**	**3**	**4**
I do not understand.	I can do it with help.	I can do it on my own.	I can teach someone else.

	Rating	Date
6.1 Scatter Plots		
Learning Target: Use scatter plots to describe patterns and relationships between two quantities.	1 2 3 4	
I can make a scatter plot.	1 2 3 4	
I can identify outliers, gaps, and clusters in a scatter plot.	1 2 3 4	
I can use scatter plots to describe relationships between data.	1 2 3 4	
6.2 Lines of Fit		
Learning Target: Use lines of fit to model data.	1 2 3 4	
I can write and interpret an equation of a line of fit.	1 2 3 4	
I can find an equation of a line of best fit.	1 2 3 4	
I can use a line of fit to make predictions.	1 2 3 4	
6.3 Two-Way Tables		
Learning Target: Use two-way tables to represent data.	1 2 3 4	
I can read a two-way table.	1 2 3 4	
I can make a two-way table.	1 2 3 4	
I can use a two-way table to describe relationships between data.	1 2 3 4	

Chapter Self-Assessment (continued)

	Rating	Date
6.4 Choosing a Data Display		
Learning Target: Use appropriate data displays to represent situations.	1 2 3 4	
I can choose appropriate data displays for situations.	1 2 3 4	
I can identify misleading data displays.	1 2 3 4	
I can analyze a variety of data displays.	1 2 3 4	

Chapter 7 Review & Refresh

Find the missing value in the table.

1.

x	y
1	5
3	7
5	9
7	

2.

x	y
2	6
4	12
8	24
12	

3.

x	y
6	11
14	19
26	31
41	

4.

x	y
8	4
18	9
28	14
38	

5.

x	y
4	2.5
11	9.5
15	13.5
21	

6.

x	y
6	5.8
15	14.8
22.8	22.6
31.4	

Big Ideas Math: Modeling Real Life Grade 7 Advanced

Chapter 7 Review & Refresh (continued)

Evaluate the expression when $x = 2, y = 3,$ and $z = -4.$

7. $3x - 2$

8. $-6 - 2y$

9. $2z^2$

10. $3y - 3z$

11. $\dfrac{8}{x} - 1$

12. $-1 + \dfrac{z}{2}$

Name_____ Date_____

7.1 Relations and Functions
For use with Exploration 7.1

Learning Target: Understand the concept of a function.

Success Criteria:
- I can represent a relation as a set of ordered pairs.
- I can determine whether a relation is a function.
- I can use functions to solve real-life problems.

1 EXPLORATION: Interpreting Diagrams

Work with a partner. Describe the relationship between the *inputs* and *outputs* in each diagram. Then complete each diagram. Is there more than one possible answer? Explain your reasoning.

a.

b.

7.1 **Relations and Functions** (continued)

2 **EXPLORATION:** Describing Relationships Between Quantities

Work with a partner. The diagrams show the numbers of tickets bought by customers for two different plays and the total costs (in dollars).

a. For each diagram, how many outputs does each input have?

b. Describe the prices of tickets for each play.

c. A person buys 4 tickets for each play. Can you determine the total cost of all 8 tickets? Explain.

Name_____ Date_____

 Notetaking with Vocabulary

Vocabulary:

Notes:

7.1 Self-Assessment

Use the scale below to rate your understanding of the learning target and the success criteria.

1	2	3	4
I do not understand.	I can do it with help.	I can do it on my own.	I can teach someone else.

	Rating	Date
7.1 Relations and Functions		
Learning Target: Understand the concept of a function.	1 2 3 4	
I can represent a relation as a set of ordered pairs.	1 2 3 4	
I can determine whether a relation is a function.	1 2 3 4	
I can use functions to solve real-life problems.	1 2 3 4	

Name _____ Date _____

7.1 Practice

List the ordered pairs shown in the mapping diagram.

1. Input   Output

2. Input   Output

Draw a mapping diagram that represents the relation. Then determine whether the relation is a function. Explain.

3.

4.

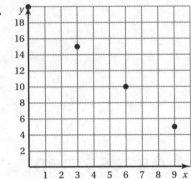

5. The table shows the cost of on-line game play.

Hours	1	2	3	4	5	6	7
Cost	$3	$3.25	$3.50	_____	_____	_____	_____

   a. Complete the table.

   b. Draw a mapping diagram for the table.

   c. Is the relation a function? Explain.

   d. List the ordered pairs.

   e. Graph the ordered pairs in a coordinate plane.

   f. Describe the pattern. How does the cost change as the number of hours increases?

Name_____ Date_____

7.2 Representations of Functions
For use with Exploration 7.2

Learning Target: Represent functions in a variety of ways.

Success Criteria:
- I can write a function rule that describes a relationship.
- I can evaluate functions for given inputs.
- I can represent functions using tables and graphs.

1 EXPLORATION: Using a Table to Describe Relationships

Work with a partner. Make a table that shows the relationship between the figure number x and the area A of each figure. Then use an equation to find which figure has an area of 81 square units when the pattern continues.

1 square unit

a.

Figure 1   Figure 2   Figure 3   Figure 4

b.

Figure 1   Figure 2   Figure 3   Figure 4

7.2 Representations of Functions (continued)

2 **EXPLORATION:** Using a Graph

Work with a partner. Use a graph to test the truth of each statement. If the statement is true, write an equation that shows how to obtain one measurement from the other.

a. "You can find the horsepower of a race-car engine if you know its volume in cubic inches."

Volume (cubic inches), x	200	350	350	500
Horsepower, y	375	650	250	600

b. "You can find the volume of a race-car engine in cubic centimeters if you know its volume in cubic inches."

Volume (cubic inches), x	100	200	300
Volume (cubic centimeters), y	1640	3280	4920

7.2 Notetaking with Vocabulary

Vocabulary:

Notes:

7.2 Self-Assessment

Use the scale below to rate your understanding of the learning target and the success criteria.

1	**2**	**3**	**4**
I do not understand.	I can do it with help.	I can do it on my own.	I can teach someone else.

	Rating	Date
7.2 Representations of Functions		
Learning Target: Represent functions in a variety of ways.	1 2 3 4	
I can write a function rule that describes a relationship.	1 2 3 4	
I can evaluate functions for given inputs.	1 2 3 4	
I can represent functions using tables and graphs.	1 2 3 4	

Name _____ Date _____

7.2 Practice

Write a function rule for the statement.

1. The output is five times the input.

2. The output is two less than the input.

Find the value of *y* for the given value of *x*.

3. $y = 3x - 4; x = 2$

4. $y = \dfrac{x}{3} - 1; x = -6$

Graph the function.

5. $y = \dfrac{x}{3} - 4$

6. $y = 2x + 7$

7. You are traveling on a turnpike at a rate of 70 miles per hour.

    a. Write a function that represents the distance *d* traveled in *h* hours.

    b. How many miles do you travel in 3.5 hours?

Find the value of *x* for the given value of *y*.

8. $y = 6x - 4; y = 20$

9. $y = \dfrac{1}{2}x + 3; y = 1$

10. Your school club is selling popcorn at the football game. The cost of making the popcorn is $90. You charge $1.50 for each bag of popcorn.

    a. Write a function you can use to find the profit *P* for selling *b* bags of popcorn.

    b. Which variable is independent? dependent? Explain.

    c. You will *break even* if the cost of making the popcorn equals your income. How many bags of popcorn must you sell to break even?

11. *s* is the side length of a square.

    a. Write a function for the perimeter *P* of a square given the side length *s* of the square.

    b. Write a function for the area *A* of a square given the perimeter *P* of the square.

12. The graph of a function is a line that passes through the points $(2, 2)$, $(4, 8)$, and $(7, y)$. What is the value of *y*?

7.3 Linear Functions
For use with Exploration 7.3

Learning Target: Use functions to model linear relationships.

Success Criteria: • I can write linear functions to model relationships.
• I can interpret linear functions in real-life situations.

1 EXPLORATION: Writing and Graphing Functions

Work with a partner. Each table shows a familiar pattern from geometry.

- **Determine what the variables x and y represent. Then write a function rule that relates y to x.**

- **Is the function a *linear function*? Explain your reasoning.**

a.

x	1	2	3	4
y	10	12	14	16

b.

x	1	2	3	4
y	π	4π	9π	16π

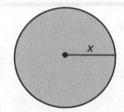

7.3 **Linear Functions** (continued)

c.

x	1	2	3	4
y	5	6	7	8

d.

x	1	2	3	4
y	28	40	52	64

7.3 Notetaking with Vocabulary

Vocabulary:

Notes:

7.3 Self-Assessment

Use the scale below to rate your understanding of the learning target and the success criteria.

1	2	3	4
I do not understand.	I can do it with help.	I can do it on my own.	I can teach someone else.

	Rating	Date
7.3 Linear Functions		
Learning Target: Use functions to model linear relationships.	1 2 3 4	
I can write linear functions to model relationships.	1 2 3 4	
I can interpret linear functions in real-life situations.	1 2 3 4	

Name _____   Date _____

Use the graph or table to write a linear function that relates _y_ to _x_.

1.

2.

3.

x	−4	−2	0	2
y	8	4	0	−4

4.

x	−5	0	5	10
y	1	3	5	7

5. The table shows the time _y_ (in minutes) it takes to make _x_ burritos.

Burritos, x	1	2	3	4
Minutes, y	0.75	1.5	2.25	3

   a. Write a linear function that relates _y_ to _x_.

   b. Graph the linear function.

   c. Interpret the slope, the _x_-intercept, and the _y_-intercept.

   d. How long does it take to make 7 burritos? Explain.

6. The table shows the distance traveled _y_ (in miles) in a car in _x_ hours.

Hours, x	0	2	4	6
Miles, y	0	128	256	384

   a. Write a linear function that relates distance traveled to hours.

   b. Graph the linear function.

   c. What was the distance traveled in 5 hours?

   d. The formula $d = rt$ relates distance with time for a given rate. Use the
   formula to determine the rate at which the car was traveling.

   e. How long will it take to travel 400 miles? Explain.

7.4 Comparing Linear and Nonlinear Functions
For use with Exploration 7.4

Learning Target: Understand differences between linear and nonlinear functions.

Success Criteria:
- I can recognize linear functions represented as tables, equations, and graphs.
- I can compare linear and nonlinear functions.

1 EXPLORATION: Comparing Functions

Work with a partner. Each equation represents the height *h* (in feet) of a falling object after *t* seconds.

- **Graph each equation. Explain your method.**

- **Decide whether each graph represents a *linear* or *nonlinear* function.**

- **Compare the falling objects.**

a. Skydiver

$$h = 300 - 15t$$

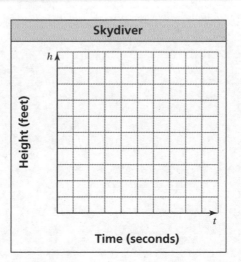

7.4 **Comparing Linear and Nonlinear Functions** (continued)

b. Bowling ball

$$h = 300 - 16t^2$$

Bowling Ball

Notetaking with Vocabulary

Vocabulary:

Notes:

 Self-Assessment

Use the scale below to rate your understanding of the learning target and the success criteria.

1	2	3	4
I do not understand.	I can do it with help.	I can do it on my own.	I can teach someone else.

	Rating	Date
7.4 Comparing Linear and Nonlinear Functions		
Learning Target: Understand differences between linear and nonlinear functions.	1 2 3 4	
I can recognize linear functions represented as tables, equations, and graphs.	1 2 3 4	
I can compare linear and nonlinear functions.	1 2 3 4	

Big Ideas Math: Modeling Real Life Grade 7 Advanced **161**
Student Journal

Name _____ Date _____

7.4 Practice

Graph the data in the table. Decide whether each graph represents a *linear* or *nonlinear* function.

1.

x	4	3	2	1
y	1	3	7	11

2.

x	2	5	8	11
y	3	6	9	12

Does the graph or equation represent a *linear* or *nonlinear* function? Explain.

3.

4.

5. $y = \frac{1}{3}x - 1$

6. $5x - y = 8$

7. The table shows the profit P (in dollars) of selling x pairs of flip flops.

Flip Flops, x	Profit, P
1	4
2	_____
3	12

   a. What is the missing P-value that makes the table represent a linear function?

   b. Write a linear function that represents the profit P of selling x pairs of flip flops. Interpret the slope.

8. The table shows the commission y (in dollars) of selling x cell phone plans.

Cell Phone Plans, x	1	2	3	4
Commission, y	100	150	250	400

   a. Does the table represent a *linear* or *nonlinear* function? Explain.

   b. Based on the pattern in the table, what is the commission of selling 5 cell phone plans?

9. The formula for the volume V of a sphere with radius r is $V = \frac{4}{3}\pi r^3$. Does this formula represent a *linear* or *nonlinear* function? Explain.

7.5 Analyzing and Sketching Graphs
For use with Exploration 7.5

Learning Target: Use graphs of functions to describe relationships between quantities.

Success Criteria:
- I can describe relationships between quantities in graphs.
- I can sketch graphs given verbal descriptions of relationships.

---

1 EXPLORATION: Matching Situations to Graphs

Work with a partner. Each graph shows your speed during a bike ride. Match each situation with its graph. Explain your reasoning.

A.

B.

C.

D.

a. You increase your speed, then ride at a constant speed along a bike path. You then slow down until you reach your friend's house.

b. You increase your speed, then go down a hill. You then quickly come to a stop at an intersection.

Big Ideas Math: Modeling Real Life Grade 7 Advanced

7.5 **Analyzing and Sketching Graphs** (continued)

    c. You increase your speed, then stop at a store for a couple of minutes. You then continue to ride, increasing your speed.

    d. You ride at a constant speed, then go up a hill. Once on top of the hill, you increase your speed.

2 **EXPLORATION:** Interpreting a Graph

Work with a partner. Write a short paragraph that describes how the height changes over time in the graph shown. What situation can this graph represent?

Notetaking with Vocabulary

Vocabulary:

Notes:

7.5 Self-Assessment

Use the scale below to rate your understanding of the learning target and the success criteria.

1	**2**	**3**	**4**
I do not understand.	I can do it with help.	I can do it on my own.	I can teach someone else.

	Rating	Date
7.5 Analyzing and Sketching Graphs		
Learning Target: Use graphs of functions to describe relationships between quantities.	1 2 3 4	
I can describe relationships between quantities in graphs.	1 2 3 4	
I can sketch graphs given verbal descriptions of relationships.	1 2 3 4	

Name _____ Date _____

7.5 Practice

Describe the relationship between the two quantities.

1. **Customers**

2. **Hiker**

3. **Postage**

4. **Water Level**

5. The supply and demand model shows how the price of the shares of a new stock changes in a market.

Demand

Supply

a. Describe and interpret each curve.

b. Which part of the graph represents a surplus? a shortage? Explain your reasoning.

c. The curve intersects at the *equilibrium point*, which is where the number of shares equals the quantity demanded. Suppose that demand for the shares suddenly increases, causing the entire demand curve to shift up. What happens to the equilibrium point?

Name_____ Date_____

Chapter 7 Chapter Self-Assessment

Use the scale below to rate your understanding of the learning target and the success criteria.

1 I do not understand. **2** I can do it with help. **3** I can do it on my own. **4** I can teach someone else.

	Rating	Date
7.1 Relations and Functions		
Learning Target: Understand the concept of a function.	1 2 3 4	
I can represent a relation as a set of ordered pairs.	1 2 3 4	
I can determine whether a relation is a function.	1 2 3 4	
I can use functions to solve real-life problems.	1 2 3 4	
7.2 Representations of Functions		
Learning Target: Represent functions in a variety of ways.	1 2 3 4	
I can write a function rule that describes a relationship.	1 2 3 4	
I can evaluate functions for given inputs.	1 2 3 4	
I can represent functions using tables and graphs.	1 2 3 4	
7.3 Linear Functions		
Learning Target: Use functions to model linear relationships.	1 2 3 4	
I can write linear functions to model relationships.	1 2 3 4	
I can interpret linear functions in real-life situations.	1 2 3 4	

Chapter 7

Chapter Self-Assessment (continued)

	Rating	Date
7.4 Comparing Linear and Nonlinear Functions		
Learning Target: Understand differences between linear and nonlinear functions.	1 2 3 4	
I can recognize linear functions represented as tables, equations, and graphs.	1 2 3 4	
I can compare linear and nonlinear functions.	1 2 3 4	
7.5 Analyzing and Sketching Graphs		
Learning Target: Use graphs of functions to describe relationships between quantities.	1 2 3 4	
I can describe relationships between quantities in graphs.	1 2 3 4	
I can sketch graphs given verbal descriptions of relationships.	1 2 3 4	

Chapter 8 Review & Refresh

Evaluate the expression.

1. $2 + 1 \cdot 4^2 - 12 \div 3$

2. $8^2 \div 16 \cdot 2 - 5$

3. $7(9 - 3) + 6^2 \cdot 10 - 8$

4. $3 \cdot 5 - 10 + 9(2 + 1)^2$

5. $8(6 + 5) - (9^2 + 3) \div 7$

6. $5[3(12 - 8)] - 6 \cdot 8 + 2^2$

7. $4 + 4 + 5 \times 2 \times 5 + (3 + 3 + 3) \times 6 \times 6 + 2 + 2$

   a. Evaluate the expression.

   b. Rewrite the expression using what you know about order of operations. Then evaluate.

Review & Refresh (continued)

Find the product or quotient.

8. $3.92 \cdot 0.6$

9. $0.78 \cdot 0.13$

10. 5.004×1.2

11. $6.3 \div 0.7$

12. $2.25 \div 1.5$

13. $8.1 \div 0.003$

14. Grapes cost \$1.98 per pound. You buy 3.5 pounds of grapes. How much do you pay for the grapes?

Name_____ Date_____

8.1 Exponents
For use with Exploration 8.1

Learning Target: Use exponents to write and evaluate expressions.

Success Criteria:
- I can write products using exponents.
- I can evaluate expressions involving powers.
- I can use exponents to solve real-life problems.

---

1 EXPLORATION: Using Exponent Notation

Work with a partner.

a. Complete the table.

Power	Repeated Multiplication Form	Value
$(-3)^1$	-3	-3
$(-3)^2$	$(-3) \cdot (-3)$	9
$(-3)^3$		
$(-3)^4$		
$(-3)^5$		
$(-3)^6$		
$(-3)^7$		

b. Describe what is meant by the expression $(-3)^n$. How can you find the value of $(-3)^n$?

8.1 **Exponents** (continued)

---

2 **EXPLORATION:** Using Exponent Notation

Work with a partner. On a game show, each small cube is worth $3. The small cubes arc arranged to form a large cube with a side length of three small cubes. Show how you can use a power to find the total value of the large cube. Then write an explanation to convince a friend that your answer is correct.

Name_____ Date_____

8.1 Notetaking with Vocabulary

Vocabulary:

Notes:

8.1 Self-Assessment

Use the scale below to rate your understanding of the learning target and the success criteria.

1	2	3	4
I do not understand.	I can do it with help.	I can do it on my own.	I can teach someone else.

	Rating	Date
8.1 Exponents		
Learning Target: Use exponents to write and evaluate expressions.	1 2 3 4	
I can write products using exponents.	1 2 3 4	
I can evaluate expressions involving powers.	1 2 3 4	
I can use exponents to solve real-life problems.	1 2 3 4	

Name _____ Date _____

8.1 Practice

Write the product using exponents.

1. $-\dfrac{3}{7} \cdot \dfrac{3}{7} \cdot \dfrac{3}{7}$

2. $\left(-\dfrac{3}{7}\right) \cdot \left(-\dfrac{3}{7}\right) \cdot \left(-\dfrac{3}{7}\right)$

3. $25 \cdot 25 \cdot 25 \cdot 25 \cdot (-p) \cdot (-p) \cdot (-p) \cdot (-p) \cdot (-p)$

4. $(-2) \cdot (-2) \cdot x \cdot x \cdot x \cdot y \cdot y \cdot y \cdot y$

Evaluate the expression.

5. 7^3

6. -4^4

7. $(-4)^4$

8. $\left(\dfrac{2}{5}\right)^3$

9. Write the prime factorization of 1323 using exponents.

Evaluate the expression.

10. $280 - (-3) \cdot (-5)^3$

11. $(20^2 - 3^3 \cdot 8^2) \div 16$

12. $\dfrac{2}{3}(16^2 - 17^2)$

13. $\left| \dfrac{1}{5} \left(\dfrac{6^3}{3^3} - 2^3 \right) \right|$

14. Bed A is 7 feet long. Bed B is $\dfrac{7}{8}$ as long as bed A. Bed C is $\dfrac{7}{8}$ as long as Bed B. Bed D is $\dfrac{7}{8}$ as long as bed C.

   a. Write an expression for the length of Bed D.

   b. What is the length of Bed D?

15. Complete the table. Compare the values of $3^h - 2$ with the values of 3^{h-1}. When are the values the same?

h	1	2	3	4	5
$3^h - 2$					
3^{h-1}					

16. You ran 8 miles. John ran half as far as you. Tim ran half as far as John. Chris ran half as far as Tim.

   a. Write an expression for how far Chris ran.

   b. How far did Chris run?

8.2 Product of Powers Property
For use with Exploration 8.2

Learning Target: Generate equivalent expressions involving products of powers.

Success Criteria:
- I can find products of powers that have the same base.
- I can find powers of powers.
- I can find powers of products.

1 EXPLORATION: Finding Products of Powers

Work with a partner.

a. Complete the table. Use your results to write a *general rule* for finding $a^m \cdot a^n$, a product of two powers with the same base.

Product	Repeated Multiplication Form	Power
$2^2 \cdot 2^4$		
$(-3)^2 \cdot (-3)^4$		
$7^3 \cdot 7^2$		
$5.1^1 \cdot 5.1^6$		
$(-4)^2 \cdot (-4)^2$		
$10^3 \cdot 10^5$		
$\left(\frac{1}{2}\right)^5 \cdot \left(\frac{1}{2}\right)^5$		

b. Show how to use your rule in part (a) to write each expression below as a single power. Then write a *general rule* for finding $(a^m)^n$, a power of a power.

$$(7^3)^2 \qquad (6^2)^2 \qquad (3^2)^3 \qquad (2^2)^4 \qquad \left(\left(\frac{1}{2}\right)^2\right)^5$$

8.2 **Product of Powers Property** (continued)

---

2 **EXPLORATION:** Finding Powers of Products

Work with a partner. Complete the table. Use your results to write a *general rule* **for finding** $(ab)^m$**, a power of a product.**

Product	Repeated Multiplication Form	Power
$(2 \cdot 3)^3$		
$(2 \cdot 5)^2$		
$(5 \cdot 4)^3$		
$(-2 \cdot 4)^2$		
$(-3 \cdot 2)^4$		

Notetaking with Vocabulary

Vocabulary:

Notes:

8.2 Self-Assessment

Use the scale below to rate your understanding of the learning target and the success criteria.

1	**2**	**3**	**4**
I do not understand.	I can do it with help.	I can do it on my own.	I can teach someone else.

	Rating	Date
8.2 Product of Powers Property		
Learning Target: Generate equivalent expressions involving products of powers.	1 2 3 4	
I can find products of powers that have the same base.	1 2 3 4	
I can find powers of powers.	1 2 3 4	
I can find powers of products.	1 2 3 4	

Name _____ Date _____

8.2 Practice

Simplify the expression. Write your answer as a power.

1. $(-16)^5 \cdot (-16)^{21}$

2. $\left(\frac{1}{15}\right)^{12} \cdot \left(\frac{1}{15}\right)$

3. $q^7 \cdot q^9$

4. $(-7.4)^9 \cdot (-7.4)^{12}$

5. $\left(\left(\frac{5}{8}\right)^2\right)^3$

6. $\left(\left(-\frac{2}{9}\right)^3\right)^5$

Simplify the expression.

7. $(-2p)^4$

8. $\left(\frac{1}{5}k\right)^3$

9. $(3^2)^4 - 3^5 \cdot 3$

10. $10\left(\frac{1}{5}v\right)^3$

11. In 2016 about $(2 \cdot 5)^4 \cdot 3^3$ text messages were sent every second. There are $2^7(3 \cdot 5)^2$ seconds in 1 day. How many text messages were sent each day in 2016? Write your answer as an expression involving three powers and in standard form.

12. The volume of a right circular cylinder is $V = \pi r^2 h$. The relationship between the height h of a given right circular cylinder and the radius r is $r = \frac{2}{3}h$.

    a. Find the volume of the right circular cylinder in terms of the height h and simplify the expression.

    b. What is the volume of the right circular cylinder when the height is $\frac{3}{4}$ inch?

    c. Find the volume of the right circular cylinder in terms of the radius r and simplify the expression.

13. Show that $(5 \cdot 27 \cdot y)^6 = 15^6 \cdot 9^6 \cdot y^6$.

Find the value of x in the equation without evaluating the power. Explain your reasoning.

14. $3^2 \cdot 3^x = 3^{12}$

15. $(5^x)^4 = 5^{24}$

16. Your boss tells you that you have to work every day in February (28 days). He gives you the choice to be paid $1000 per day or 2^x cents per day, where x is the day of the month. Which payment method do you choose? What is the total amount of money you get paid at the end of the month?

178 **Big Ideas Math: Modeling Real Life Grade 7 Advanced**
Student Journal

8.3 Quotient of Powers Property
For use with Exploration 8.3

Learning Target: Generate equivalent expressions involving quotients of powers.

Success Criteria:
- I can find quotients of powers that have the same base.
- I can simplify expressions using the Quotient of Powers Property.
- I can solve real-life problems involving quotients of powers.

1 EXPLORATION: Finding Quotients of Powers

Work with a partner.

a. Complete the table. Use your results to write a *general rule* for finding $\frac{a^m}{a^n}$, a quotient of two powers with the same base.

Product	Repeated Multiplication Form	Power
$\dfrac{2^4}{2^2}$	$\dfrac{2 \cdot 2 \cdot 2 \cdot 2}{2 \cdot 2}$	
$\dfrac{(-4)^5}{(-4)^2}$		
$\dfrac{7^7}{7^3}$		
$\dfrac{8.5^9}{8.5^6}$		
$\dfrac{10^8}{10^5}$		
$\dfrac{3^{12}}{3^4}$		
$\dfrac{(-5)^7}{(-5)^5}$		
$\dfrac{11^4}{11^1}$		
$\dfrac{x^6}{x^2}$		

8.3 **Quotient of Powers Property** (continued)

b. Use your rule in part (a) to simplify the quotients in the first column of the table above. Does your rule give the results in the third column?

Notetaking with Vocabulary

Vocabulary:

Notes:

 Self-Assessment

Use the scale below to rate your understanding of the learning target and the success criteria.

1	**2**	**3**	**4**
I do not understand.	I can do it with help.	I can do it on my own.	I can teach someone else.

	Rating	Date
8.3 Quotient of Powers Property		
Learning Target: Generate equivalent expressions involving quotients of powers.	1　2　3　4	
I can find quotients of powers that have the same base.	1　2　3　4	
I can simplify expressions using the Quotient of Powers Property.	1　2　3　4	
I can solve real-life problems involving quotients of powers.	1　2　3　4	

8.3 Practice

Simplify the expression. Write your answer as a power.

1. $\dfrac{7.6^{13}}{7.6^3}$

2. $\dfrac{u^{33}}{u^{11}}$

3. One kilometer equals 10^3 meters. One tetrameter equals 10^{12} meters.

    a. How many times larger is a tetrameter than a kilometer?

    b. A square has side length of 1 kilometer. Find the area in meters. Write your answer as a power.

    c. A square has side length of 1 tetrameter. Find the area in meters. Write your answer as a power.

    d. How many times larger is the area of the square in part (c) than the area of the square in part (b)?

    e. A cube has side length of 1 kilometer. Find the volume in meters. Write your answer as a power.

    f. A cube has side length of 1 tetrameter. Find the volume in meters. Write your answer as a power.

    g. How many times larger is the volume of the cube in part (e) than the volume of the cube in part (f)?

Simplify the expression. Write your answer as a power.

4. $\dfrac{(-7.9)^{15} \cdot (-7.9)^9}{(-7.9)^{12} \cdot (-7.9)^7}$

5. $\dfrac{b^{35}}{b^{20}} \cdot \dfrac{b^{15}}{b^{10}}$

Determine whether the statement is *always*, *never*, or *sometimes* true. Explain your reasoning.

6. The expression $\dfrac{5^{x+3}}{5^x}$ will equal 5^3.

7. The expression $\dfrac{5^x}{5^y}$ will equal 5^3.

8. The expression $\dfrac{5^{x+1}}{5^x}$ will equal 5^3.

Find the value of x in the equation without evaluating the power.

9. $\dfrac{9^7}{9^x} = 729$

10. $\dfrac{2^{12} \cdot 2^x}{2^{10}} = 32$

8.4 Zero and Negative Exponents
For use with Exploration 8.4

Learning Target: Understand the concepts of zero and negative exponents.

Success Criteria:
- I can explain the meanings of zero and negative exponents.
- I can evaluate numerical expressions involving zero and negative exponents.
- I can simplify algebraic expressions involving zero and negative exponents.

---

1 EXPLORATION: Understanding Zero Exponents

Work with a partner.

a. Complete the table.

Quotient	Quotient of Powers Property	Power
$\dfrac{5^3}{5^3}$		
$\dfrac{6^2}{6^2}$		
$\dfrac{(-3)^4}{(-3)^4}$		
$\dfrac{(-4)^5}{(-4)^5}$		

b. Evaluate each expression in the first column of the table in part (a). How can you use these results to define a^0, where $a \neq 0$?

8.4 **Zero and Negative Exponents** (continued)

2 **EXPLORATION:** Understanding Negative Exponents

Work with a partner.

a. Complete the table.

Product	Product of Powers Property	Power	Value
$5^{-3} \cdot 5^3$			
$6^2 \cdot 6^{-2}$			
$(-3)^4 \cdot (-3)^{-4}$			
$(-4)^{-5} \cdot (-4)^5$			

b. How can you use the Multiplicative Inverse Property to rewrite the powers containing negative exponents in the first column of the table?

c. Use your results in parts (a) and (b) to define a^{-n}, where $a \neq 0$ and n is an integer.

8.4 Notetaking with Vocabulary

Vocabulary:

Notes:

8.4 Self-Assessment

Use the scale below to rate your understanding of the learning target and the success criteria.

1	2	3	4
I do not understand.	I can do it with help.	I can do it on my own.	I can teach someone else.

	Rating	Date
8.4 Zero and Negative Exponents		
Learning Target: Understand the concepts of zero and negative exponents.	1 2 3 4	
I can explain the meanings of zero and negative exponents.	1 2 3 4	
I can evaluate numerical expressions involving zero and negative exponents.	1 2 3 4	
I can simplify algebraic expressions involving zero and negative exponents.	1 2 3 4	

8.4 Practice

Evaluate the expression.

1. $10^{-1} \cdot 10^{-2}$

2. $\dfrac{1}{3^{-4}} \cdot \dfrac{1}{3^6}$

3. $27^{-18} \cdot 27^{18}$

4. $\dfrac{4^{-7}}{4^2 \cdot 4^{-5}}$

5. Write three different powers with negative exponents that are equal to 64^{-1}.

6. One millimeter equals 10^{-3} meter. One picometer equals 10^{-12} meter. One femtometer equals 10^{-15} meter.

   a. Find the product of one millimeter and one picometer, using only positive exponents.

   b. Find the quotient of one picometer and one millimeter, using only positive exponents.

   c. Find the product of one millimeter and one femtometer, using only positive exponents.

   d. Find the quotient of one femtometer and one picometer, using only positive exponents.

   e. Find the quotient of one picometer and one femtometer, using only positive exponents.

   f. Find the quotient of one millimeter and one femtometer, using only positive exponents.

   g. Find the product of one picometer and one femtometer, using only positive exponents.

Simplify. Write the expression using only positive exponents.

7. $\dfrac{14u^{-4}}{7u^8}$

8. $\dfrac{2^{-3} \cdot a^0 \cdot b^5}{b^{-4}}$

9. A swimming pool contains 6.8×10^3 gallons of water. The pool is leaking at a rate of 12^{-1} gallons per second. How many hours will it take for all of the water to leak out of the pool?

8.5 Estimating Quantities
For use with Exploration 8.5

Learning Target: Round numbers and write the results as the product of a single digit and a power of 10.

Success Criteria:
- I can round very large and very small numbers.
- I can write a multiple of 10 as a power.
- I can compare very large or very small quantities.

---

1 EXPLORATION: Using Powers of 10

Work with a partner. Match each picture with the most appropriate distance. Explain your reasoning.

6×10^3 m	1×10^1 m	2×10^{-1} m	6×10^{-2} m

a.

b.

c.

d.

8.5 **Estimating Quantities** (continued)

---

2 **EXPLORATION:** Approximating Numbers

Work with a partner. Match each number in List 1 with its closest approximation in List 2. Explain your method.

	List 1		*List 2*
a.	180,000,000,000,000	**A.**	3×10^{11}
b.	0.0000000011	**B.**	1×10^{-5}
c.	302,000,000,000	**C.**	2×10^{14}
d.	0.00000028	**D.**	3×10^{13}
e.	0.0000097	**E.**	3×10^{-7}
f.	330,000,000,000,000	**F.**	1×10^{-9}
g.	26,000,000,000,000	**G.**	2×10^{-5}
h.	0.000023	**H.**	3×10^{14}

Notetaking with Vocabulary

Vocabulary:

Notes:

8.5 Self-Assessment

Use the scale below to rate your understanding of the learning target and the success criteria.

1	**2**	**3**	**4**
I do not understand.	I can do it with help.	I can do it on my own.	I can teach someone else.

	Rating	Date
8.5 Estimating Quantities		
Learning Target: Round numbers and write the results as the product of a single digit and a power of 10.	1 2 3 4	
I can round very large and very small numbers.	1 2 3 4	
I can write a multiple of 10 as a power.	1 2 3 4	
I can compare very large or very small quantities.	1 2 3 4	

8.5 Practice

Round the number. Write the result as a product of a single digit and a power of 10.

1. 63,208,510,000

2. 45,007,899

3. Your neighbor is one of the winners of the lottery. Your neighbor's share of the winnings is $674,385. Write the result as a product of a single digit and a power of 10.

Round the number. Write the result as a product of a single digit and a power of 10.

4. 0.000000528

5. 0.00000000007398

6. The files on your computer contain about 3,894,467 words. The files on your friend's computer contain about 2.5 times the number of words as the files on your computer. What is the approximate number of words on your friend's computer?

7. The distance of a marathon running race is about 42,164.81 meters. The distance of a Ragnar relay race is about 7.5 times this distance.

   a. What is the approximate distance of a Ragnar relay race?

   b. A Ragnar relay team consists of 6 runners. If each runner runs the same distance, approximately how far will each runner run?

   c. Write the result in part (b) as the product of a single digit and a power of 10.

8. Is 7×10^{-5} a better approximation of 0.00006973 or 0.00007271? Explain.

9. The surface area of Lake Ontario is about 204,070,000,000 square feet and the surface area of Lake Superior is about 883,745,000,000 square feet. Approximately how many times greater is the surface area of Lake Superior than the surface area of Lake Ontario?

10. Find a number that is 3.5 times 41,582,915,200. Write the result as the product of a single digit and a power of 10.

11. Your phone has about 784,392 bytes of storage left. Is this more or less than 1 megabyte of storage? (1 megabyte = 10^6) Explain.

8.6 Scientific Notation
For use with Exploration 8.6

Learning Target: Understand the concept of scientific notation.

Success Criteria:
- I can convert between scientific notation and standard form.
- I can choose appropriate units to represent quantities.
- I can use scientific notation to solve real-life problems.

---

1 EXPLORATION: Using a Graphing Calculator

Work with a partner. Use a graphing calculator.

a. Experiment with multiplying very large numbers until your calculator displays an answer that is *not* in standard form. What do you think the answer means?

b. Enter the function $y = 10^x$ into your graphing calculator. Use the *table* feature to evaluate the function for positive integer values of x until the calculator displays a y-value that is not in standard form. Do the results support your answer in part (a)? Explain.

8.6 Scientific Notation (continued)

c. Repeat part (a) with very small numbers.

d. Enter the function $y = \left(\frac{1}{10}\right)^x$ into your graphing calculator. Use the *table* feature to evaluate the function for positive integer values of x until the calculator displays a y-value that is not in standard form. Do the results support your answer in part (c)? Explain.

8.6 Notetaking with Vocabulary

Vocabulary:

Notes:

8.6 Self-Assessment

Use the scale below to rate your understanding of the learning target and the success criteria.

1	**2**	**3**	**4**
I do not understand.	I can do it with help.	I can do it on my own.	I can teach someone else.

	Rating	Date
8.6 Scientific Notation		
Learning Target: Understand the concept of scientific notation.	1 2 3 4	
I can convert between scientific notation and standard form.	1 2 3 4	
I can choose appropriate units to represent quantities.	1 2 3 4	
I can use scientific notation to solve real-life problems.	1 2 3 4	

8.6 Practice

Write the number in scientific notation.

1. 0.000085

2. 410,000,000

3. 7,000,000,000,000,000

4. 0.00000000000199

Write the number in standard form.

5. 5×10^{-4}

6. 1.54×10^5

7. 1.78×10^{-6}

8. 3.555×10^8

9. The radius of Earth is about 6.38×10^6 meters. The radius of the Moon is about 1.74×10^6 meters. The radius of the Sun is about 7×10^8 meters.

   a. Which is the largest, *Earth*, the *Moon*, or the *Sun*?

   b. Which is the smallest, *Earth*, the *Moon*, or the *Sun*?

   c. Write the radius of Earth in standard form.

   d. Write the radius of the Moon in standard form.

   e. Write the radius of the Sun in standard form.

10. A year is about 3.156×10^7 seconds.

    a. How many seconds are in 5 years? Write your answer in standard form.

    b. How many seconds are in 1 month? Write your answer in standard form.

11. Approximately how many moons would be needed side-by-side to span across the Sun?

    Sun

    Moon

    1.392×10^6 km 3.475×10^3 km

    not drawn to scale

12. Most golf balls have about 250 to 450 dimples. The record holder is a ball with 1070 dimples.

    a. Write 1070 in scientific notation.

    b. In a recent year, it was estimated that 540,000,000 golf balls were sold. Using an average of 350 dimples, how many dimples were on the golf balls sold in that year? Write your answer in scientific notation.

8.7 Operations in Scientific Notation
For use with Exploration 8.7

Learning Target: Perform operations with numbers written in scientific notation.

Success Criteria:
- I can explain how to add and subtract numbers in scientific notation.
- I can explain how to multiply and divide numbers in scientific notation.
- I can use operations in scientific notation to solve real-life problems.

1 EXPLORATION: Adding and Subtracting in Scientific Notation

Work with a partner.

a. Complete the table by finding the sum and the difference of Expression 1 and Expression 2. Write your answers in scientific notation. Explain your method.

Expression 1	Expression 2	Sum	Difference
3×10^4	1×10^4		
4×10^{-3}	2×10^{-3}		
4.1×10^{-7}	1.5×10^{-7}		
8.3×10^6	1.5×10^6		

b. Use your results in part (a) to explain how to find $(a \times 10^n) + (b \times 10^n)$ and $(a \times 10^n) - (b \times 10^n)$.

8.7   Operations in Scientific Notation (continued)

---

2   **EXPLORATION:** Multiplying and Dividing in Scientific Notation

Work with a partner.

   a. Complete the table by finding the product and the quotient of Expression 1 and Expression 2. Write your answers in scientific notation. Explain your method.

Expression 1	Expression 2	Product	Quotient
3×10^4	1×10^4		
4×10^3	2×10^2		
7.7×10^{-2}	1.1×10^{-3}		
4.5×10^5	3×10^{-1}		

   b. Use your results in part (a) to explain how to find $(a \times 10^n) \times (b \times 10^m)$ and $(a \times 10^n) \div (b \times 10^m)$. Describe any properties that you use.

Notetaking with Vocabulary

Vocabulary:

Notes:

8.7 **Self-Assessment**

Use the scale below to rate your understanding of the learning target and the success criteria.

1	**2**	**3**	**4**
I do not understand.	I can do it with help.	I can do it on my own.	I can teach someone else.

	Rating	Date
8.7 Operations in Scientific Notation		
Learning Target: Perform operations with numbers written in scientific notation.	1 2 3 4	
I can explain how to add and subtract numbers in scientific notation.	1 2 3 4	
I can explain how to multiply and divide numbers in scientific notation.	1 2 3 4	
I can use operations in scientific notation to solve real-life problems.	1 2 3 4	

Name_____ Date _____

8.7 Practice

Find the sum or difference. Write your answer in scientific notation.

1. $(1.4 \times 10^2) - (1.1 \times 10^2)$

2. $(5.2 \times 10^{-4}) - (4.58 \times 10^{-4})$

3. $(6.4 \times 10^{-2}) + (4.7 \times 10^{-3})$

4. $(5.92 \times 10^{14}) - (3 \times 10^{12})$

Find the product or quotient. Write your answer in scientific notation.

5. $(7.5 \times 10^{-5}) \div (3 \times 10^{-3})$

6. $(6.1 \times 10^{-6}) \times (3 \times 10^{-1})$

7. $(6.8 \times 10^{-14}) \div (8.5 \times 10^{10})$

8. $(6 \times 10^{-8}) \times (3.1 \times 10^{12})$

Find the area of the figure. Write your answer in scientific notation.

9.

5.2×10^4 m

2.7×10^8 m

Not drawn to scale

10.

3.4×10^{-4} ft

7.8×10^{-6} ft

Not drawn to scale

11. How many times greater is the total area of Russia than the total area of Finland?

Finland
Total Area ≈ 3.4×10^5 km^2

Russia
Total Area ≈ 1.7×10^7 km^2

Evaluate the expression. Write your answer in scientific notation.

12. $48{,}000{,}000 \div (1.6 \times 10^3) + (2.7 \times 10^4)$

13. $(1.9 \times 10^9) - 6{,}300{,}000 \times (5.6 \times 10^2)$

14. You use technology and find a sum of 6.712E–8. Write this sum in standard form.

Name_____ Date_____

Chapter Self-Assessment

Use the scale below to rate your understanding of the learning target and the success criteria.

1	**2**	**3**	**4**
I do not understand.	I can do it with help.	I can do it on my own.	I can teach someone else.

	Rating	Date
8.1 Exponents		
Learning Target: Use exponents to write and evaluate expressions.	1 2 3 4	
I can write products using exponents.	1 2 3 4	
I can evaluate expressions involving powers.	1 2 3 4	
I can use exponents to solve real-life problems.	1 2 3 4	
8.2 Product of Powers Property		
Learning Target: Generate equivalent expressions involving products of powers.	1 2 3 4	
I can find products of powers that have the same base.	1 2 3 4	
I can find powers of powers.	1 2 3 4	
I can find powers of products.	1 2 3 4	
8.3 Quotient of Powers Property		
Learning Target: Generate equivalent expressions involving quotients of powers.	1 2 3 4	
I can find quotients of powers that have the same base.	1 2 3 4	
I can simplify expressions using the Quotient of Powers Property.	1 2 3 4	
I can solve real-life problems involving quotients of powers.	1 2 3 4	

Chapter 8 Chapter Self-Assessment (continued)

	Rating	Date
8.4 Zero and Negative Exponents		
Learning Target: Understand the concepts of zero and negative exponents.	1 2 3 4	
I can explain the meanings of zero and negative exponents.	1 2 3 4	
I can evaluate numerical expressions involving zero and negative exponents.	1 2 3 4	
I can simplify algebraic expressions involving zero and negative exponents.	1 2 3 4	
8.5 Estimating Quantities		
Learning Target: Round numbers and write the results as the product of a single digit and a power of 10.	1 2 3 4	
I can round very large and very small numbers.	1 2 3 4	
I can write a multiple of 10 as a power.	1 2 3 4	
I can compare very large or very small quantities.	1 2 3 4	
8.6 Scientific Notation		
Learning Target: Understand the concept of scientific notation.	1 2 3 4	
I can convert between scientific notation and standard form.	1 2 3 4	
I can choose appropriate units to represent quantities.	1 2 3 4	
I can use scientific notation to solve real-life problems.	1 2 3 4	
8.7 Operations in Scientific Notation		
Learning Target: Perform operations with numbers written in scientific notation.	1 2 3 4	
I can explain how to add and subtract numbers in scientific notation.	1 2 3 4	
I can explain how to multiply and divide numbers in scientific notation.	1 2 3 4	
I can use operations in scientific notation to solve real-life problems.	1 2 3 4	

Name_____ Date_____

Complete the number sentence with <, >, or =.

1. 3.4 _____ 3.45

2. −6.01 _____ − 6.1

3. 3.50 _____ 3.5

4. −0.84 _____ − 0.91

Find three decimals that make the number sentence true.

5. −5.2 ≥ _____

6. 2.65 > _____

7. −3.18 ≤ _____

8. 0.03 < _____

9. The table shows the times of a 100-meter dash. Order the runners from first place to fifth place.

Runner	Time (seconds)
A	12.60
B	12.55
C	12.49
D	12.63
E	12.495

Evaluate the expression.

10. $10^2 - 48 \div 6 + 25 \cdot 3$

11. $8\left(\frac{16}{4}\right) + 2^2 - 11 \cdot 3$

12. $\left(\frac{6}{3} + 4\right)^2 \div 4 \cdot 7$

13. $5(9 - 4)^2 - 3^2$

14. $5^2 - 2^2 \cdot 4^2 - 12$

15. $\left(\frac{50}{5^2}\right)^2 \div 4$

16. The table shows the numbers of students in 4 classes. The teachers are combining the classes and dividing the students in half to form two groups for a project. Write an expression to represent this situation. How many students are in each group?

Class	Students
1	24
2	32
3	30
4	28

Name_____ Date _____

Learning Target: Understand the concept of a square root of a number.

Success Criteria:
- I can find square roots of numbers.
- I can evaluate expressions involving square roots.
- I can use square roots to solve equations.

1 EXPLORATION: Finding Side Lengths

Work with a partner. Find the side length s of each square. Explain your method.

Area = 81 yd²

s

s

Area = 324 cm²

s

s

Area = 361 mi²

s

s

Area = 225 mi²

s

s

Area = 2.89 in.²

s

s

Area = $\frac{4}{9}$ ft²

s

s

9.1 **Finding Square Roots** (continued)

---

2 **EXPLORATION:** Finding Solutions of Equations

Work with a partner. Use mental math to solve each equation. How many solutions are there for each equation? Explain your reasoning.

$x^2 = 0$

$x^2 = 1$

$x^2 = 4$

$x^2 = 9$

$x^2 = 16$

$x^2 = 25$

9.1 Notetaking with Vocabulary

Vocabulary:

Notes:

9.1 Self-Assessment

Use the scale below to rate your understanding of the learning target and the success criteria.

1 I do not understand.

2 I can do it with help.

3 I can do it on my own.

4 I can teach someone else.

	Rating	Date
9.1 Finding Square Roots		
Learning Target: Understand the concept of a square root of a number.	1 2 3 4	
I can find square roots of numbers.	1 2 3 4	
I can evaluate expressions involving square roots.	1 2 3 4	
I can use square roots to solve equations.	1 2 3 4	

9.1 Practice

Find the dimensions of the square or circle.

1. Area $= \frac{169}{225}$ cm^2

2. Area $= 121\pi$ yd^2

3. You have a square plot of land that has an area of 144 square feet. You want to plant the largest circular flower garden possible on the plot of land. What is the area of the flower garden? Use 3.14 for π.

Find the square root(s).

4. $-\sqrt{484}$

5. $\pm\sqrt{\frac{25}{64}}$

6. A cylindrical oil tank holds about 785 cubic feet of oil and has a height of 10 feet. The formula for the volume of a cylinder is $V = \pi r^2 h$. Find the radius of the tank. Use 3.14 for π.

Evaluate the expression.

7. $6\sqrt{2.25} - 4.2$

8. $3\left(\sqrt{\frac{48}{3}} - 2\right)$

Copy and complete the statement with <, >, or =.

9. $\sqrt{\frac{49}{9}}$ ____ 2

10. $\frac{2}{5}$ ____ $\sqrt{\frac{12}{75}}$

11. The area of a sector of a circle is represented by $A = \frac{5}{18}\pi r^2$, where r is the radius of the circle (in meters). What is the radius when the area is 40π square meters?

12. Two squares are drawn. The smaller square has an area of 256 square meters. The areas of the two squares have a ratio of 4 : 9. What is the side length s of the larger square?

13. The cost C (in dollars) of producing x DVD players is represented by $C = 4.5x^2$. How many DVD players are produced if the cost is $544.50?

9.2 The Pythagorean Theorem
For use with Exploration 9.2

Learning Target: Understand the Pythagorean Theorem.

Success Criteria:
- I can explain the Pythagorean Theorem.
- I can use the Pythagorean Theorem to find unknown side lengths of triangles.
- I can use the Pythagorean Theorem to find distances between points in a coordinate plane.

---

1 EXPLORATION: Discovering the Pythagorean Theorem

Work with a partner.

- **On grid paper, draw a right triangle with one horizontal side and one vertical side.**

- **Label the lengths of the two shorter sides a and b. Label the length of the longest side c.**

- **Draw three squares that each share a side with your triangle. Label the areas of the squares a^2, b^2, and c^2.**

- **Cut out each square. Then make eight copies of the right triangle and cut them out (*).**

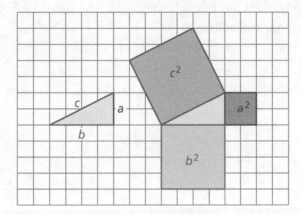

* Figures are available in the back of the Student Journal.

9.2 **The Pythagorean Theorem** (continued)

    a. Arrange the figures to show how a^2 and b^2 relate to c^2. Use an equation to represent this relationship.

    b. Estimate the side length c of your triangle. Then use the relationship in part (a) to find c. Compare the values.

Notetaking with Vocabulary

Vocabulary:

Notes:

 Self-Assessment

Use the scale below to rate your understanding of the learning target and the success criteria.

1	**2**	**3**	**4**
I do not understand.	I can do it with help.	I can do it on my own.	I can teach someone else.

	Rating	Date
9.2 The Pythagorean Theorem		
Learning Target: Understand the Pythagorean Theorem	1 2 3 4	
I can explain the Pythagorean Theorem.	1 2 3 4	
I can use the Pythagorean Theorem to find unknown side lengths of triangles.	1 2 3 4	
I can use the Pythagorean Theorem to find distances between points in a coordinate plane.	1 2 3 4	

Name _____ Date _____

9.2 Practice

Find the missing length of the triangle.

1.

35 mm   c

12 mm

2.

8.75 ft

a

9.25 ft

3. You built braces in the shape of a right triangle to hold your surfboard. The leg (brace) attached to the wall is 10 inches and your surfboard sits on a leg that is 24 inches. What is the length of the hypotenuse that completes the right triangle?

4. Laptops are advertised by the lengths of the diagonals of the screen. You purchase a 15-inch laptop and the width of the screen is 12 inches. What is the height of its screen?

5. In a right isosceles triangle, the lengths of both legs are equal. For the given isosceles triangle, what is the value of x?

x x

$\sqrt{72}$ cm

6. To get from your house to your school, you ride your bicycle 6 blocks west and 8 blocks north. A new road is being built that will go directly from your house to your school, creating a right triangle. When you take the new road to school, how many fewer blocks will you be riding to school and back?

8 blocks   c

6 blocks

7. The points A, B and C are the vertices of a triangle. The coordinates of the points are A(5,3) , B(5,6) and C(x,3). Find two values for x so the points form a right triangle.

8. The legs of a right triangle have lengths of 15 feet and 36 feet. The hypotenuse has a length of $13x$ feet. What is the value of x?

9. You have a box that is a cube with side length of 10 cm. Will a pencil that is 17 cm long fit inside the box? Explain your reasoning.

Name_____ Date_____

9.3 Finding Cube Roots
For use with Exploration 9.3

Learning Target: Understand the concept of a cube root of a number.

Success Criteria:
- I can find cube roots of numbers.
- I can evaluate expressions involving cube roots.
- I can use cube roots to solve equations.

1 EXPLORATION: Finding Edge Lengths

Work with a partner. Find the edge length s of each cube. Explain your method.

Volume = 8 cm³

Volume = 27 ft³

Volume = 125 m³

Volume = 343 in.³

Volume = 0.001 cm³

Volume = $\frac{1}{8}$ yd³

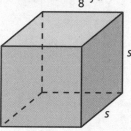

9.3 **Finding Cube Roots** (continued)

---

2 **EXPLORATION:** Finding Solutions of Equations

Work with a partner. Use mental math to solve each equation. How many solutions are there for each equation? Explain your reasoning.

$$x^3 = -27$$

$$x^3 = -8$$

$$x^3 = -1$$

$$x^3 = 1$$

$$x^3 = 8$$

$$x^3 = 27$$

Name_____ Date _____

 Notetaking with Vocabulary

Vocabulary:

Notes:

9.3 **Self-Assessment**

Use the scale below to rate your understanding of the learning target and the success criteria.

1	2	3	4
I do not understand.	I can do it with help.	I can do it on my own.	I can teach someone else.

	Rating	Date
9.3 Finding Cube Roots		
Learning Target: Understand the concept of a cube root of a number	1 2 3 4	
I can find cube roots of numbers.	1 2 3 4	
I can evaluate expressions involving cube roots.	1 2 3 4	
I can use cube roots to solve equations.	1 2 3 4	

Name _____ Date _____

Find the cube root.

1. $\sqrt[3]{343}$

2. $\sqrt[3]{-1331}$

3. $\sqrt[3]{-\dfrac{125}{27}}$

Evaluate the expression.

4. $13 + \left(\sqrt[3]{125}\right)^3$

5. $2\dfrac{2}{3} - \left(\sqrt[3]{\dfrac{1}{27}}\right)^3$

6. $24 + \left(\sqrt[3]{-1000}\right)^3$

Evaluate the expression for the given value of the variable.

7. $\sqrt[3]{4t} + 3t, t = 54$

8. $\sqrt[3]{\dfrac{n}{24}} - \dfrac{n}{25}, n = 375$

9. The volume of a storage pod that is shaped like a cube is 1728 cubic feet.

    a. What is the edge length of the storage pod?

    b. What is the surface area of the storage pod?

    c. What is the area of the floor space of the storage pod?

Copy and complete the statement with <, >, or =.

10. 0.25 _____ $\sqrt[3]{0.008}$

11. $\sqrt{729}$ _____ $\sqrt[3]{729}$

12. There are infinitely many pairs of numbers of which the sum of their cube roots is zero. Give two of these pairs.

13. The radius of a sphere can be represented by $r = \sqrt[3]{\dfrac{3V}{4\pi}}$, where V is the volume of the sphere. What is the radius of a sphere with a volume of 36π cubic meters?

Solve the equation.

14. $(4x - 1)^3 = 343$

15. $(15x^3 - 2)^3 = 2197$

16. The ratio $x : 8$ is equivalent to the ratio $27 : x^2$. What is the value of x?

Name_____ Date_____

9.4 Rational Numbers
For use with Exploration 9.4

Learning Target: Convert between different forms of rational numbers.

Success Criteria:
- I can explain the meaning of rational numbers.
- I can write fractions and mixed numbers as decimals.
- I can write repeating decimals as fractions or mixed numbers.

---

1 **EXPLORATION: Writing Repeating Decimals as Fractions**

Work with a partner.

a. Complete the table.

x	$10x$
$x = 0.333\ldots$	$10x = 3.333\ldots$
$x = 0.666\ldots$	
$x = 0.111\ldots$	
$x = 0.2444\ldots$	

b. For each row of the table, use the two equations and what you know about solving systems of equations to write a third equation that does not involve a repeating decimal. Then solve the equation. What does your solution represent?

9.4 **Rational Numbers** (continued)

c. Write each repeating decimal below as a fraction. How is your procedure similar to parts (a) and (b)? How is it different?

$x = 0.\overline{12}$

$x = 0.\overline{45}$

$x = 0.\overline{27}$

$x = 0.9\overline{40}$

d. Explain how to write a repeating decimal with n repeating digits as a fraction.

Name_____ Date_____

9.4 Notetaking with Vocabulary

Vocabulary:

Notes:

9.4 Self-Assessment

Use the scale below to rate your understanding of the learning target and the success criteria.

1	2	3	4
I do not understand.	I can do it with help.	I can do it on my own.	I can teach someone else.

	Rating	Date
9.4 Rational Numbers		
Learning Target: Convert between different forms of rational numbers.	1 2 3 4	
I can explain the meaning of rational numbers.	1 2 3 4	
I can write fractions and mixed numbers as decimals.	1 2 3 4	
I can write repeating decimals as fractions or mixed numbers.	1 2 3 4	

9.4 Practice

Write the fraction or mixed number as a decimal.

1. $\dfrac{7}{36}$

2. $-7\dfrac{4}{75}$

3. $3\dfrac{2}{11}$

4. The length of your computer mouse is $4\dfrac{7}{16}$ inches long. Write this length as a decimal.

Write the repeating decimal as a fraction or a mixed number.

5. $8.\overline{7}$

6. $24.\overline{8}$

7. $-1.4\overline{5}$

8. $-0.\overline{32}$

9. $6.\overline{13}$

10. $7.\overline{90}$

11. The probability of rolling a 5 when rolling a 6-sided die is $0.1\overline{66}$. Write this probability as a fraction.

12. You are making two types of cookies for the math club bake sale.

   a. The recipe for Cookie A uses 0.6 times the amount of flour used in the recipe for Cookie B. The recipe for Cookie B calls for $3\dfrac{2}{3}$ cups of flour. How many cups of flour should you buy to have enough for both recipes?

   b. Both recipes call for $0.\overline{66}$ cups of brown sugar. How many cups of brown sugar should you buy to have enough for both recipes? Write this number as a fraction.

   c. The recipe for Cookie B uses $\dfrac{3}{4}$ times the amount of butter used in the recipe for Cookie A. The recipe for Cookie A calls for $1.08\overline{33}$ cups of butter. How many cups of butter should you buy to have enough for both recipes? Write this number as a decimal.

Add or subtract.

13. $0.3\overline{05} + 0.2\overline{41}$

14. $\dfrac{7}{44} - 0.\overline{99}$

15. $0.\overline{01} - 0.\overline{05}$

16. Write a repeating decimal that is between $\dfrac{3}{11}$ and $\dfrac{4}{11}$. Justify your answer.

17. Write two repeating decimals that $\dfrac{17}{30}$ falls between. Justify your answer.

Determine whether the numbers are equal. Justify your answer.

18. $\dfrac{7}{33}$ and 0.21

19. $\dfrac{5}{44}$ and $0.11\overline{36}$

20. $\dfrac{6}{55}$ and $0.1\overline{09}$

9.5 Irrational Numbers
For use with Exploration 9.5

Learning Target: Understand the concept of irrational numbers.

Success Criteria:
- I can classify real numbers as rational or irrational.
- I can approximate irrational numbers.
- I can solve real-life problems involving irrational numbers.

1 EXPLORATION: Approximating Square Roots

Work with a partner. Use the square shown.

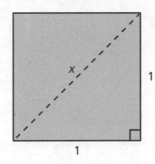

a. Find the exact length x of the diagonal. Is this number a *rational number* or an *irrational number*? Explain.

b. The value of x is between which two whole numbers? Explain your reasoning.

9.5 Irrational Numbers (continued)

c. Use the diagram below (*) to approximate the length of the diagonal to the nearest tenth. Explain your method.

d. Which of the following is the closest approximation of the length of the diagonal? Justify your answer using inverse operations.

| 1.412 | | 1.413 | | 1.414 | | 1.415 |

* Diagram is available in the back of the Student Journal.

9.5 Notetaking with Vocabulary

Vocabulary:

Notes:

9.5 Self-Assessment

Use the scale below to rate your understanding of the learning target and the success criteria.

1	2	3	4
I do not understand.	I can do it with help.	I can do it on my own.	I can teach someone else.

	Rating	Date
9.5 Irrational Numbers		
Learning Target: Understand the concept of irrational numbers.	1 2 3 4	
I can classify real numbers as rational or irrational.	1 2 3 4	
I can approximate irrational numbers.	1 2 3 4	
I can solve real-life problems involving irrational numbers.	1 2 3 4	

Name _____ Date _____

9.5 Practice

Classify the real number.

1. $2\frac{2}{9}$

2. $-\sqrt{576}$

3. $2.\overline{41}$

4. $\sqrt{130}$

5. You are finding the circumference of a circle with a diameter of 10 meters. Is the circumference a *rational* or *irrational* number? Explain.

Approximate the number to the nearest (a) integer and (b) tenth.

6. $-\sqrt{\dfrac{250}{9}}$

7. $\sqrt{395}$

8. $\sqrt[3]{-50}$

9. $\sqrt{0.79}$

10. $\sqrt{1.48}$

11. $\sqrt[3]{294}$

12. A patio is in the shape of a square, with a side length of 35 feet. You wish to draw a black line down one diagonal.

   a. Use the Pythagorean Theorem to find the length of the diagonal. Write your answer as a square root.

   b. Find the two perfect squares that the length of the diagonal falls between.

   c. Estimate the length of the diagonal to the nearest tenth.

Which number is greater? Explain.

13. $\sqrt{220}, \sqrt[3]{1260}$

14. $-\sqrt{135}, -\sqrt{145}$

15. $\sqrt{\dfrac{7}{64}}, \sqrt[3]{\dfrac{1}{28}}$

16. $2\pi, \sqrt[3]{250}$

17. Find two numbers a and b such that $7 < \sqrt{a} < \sqrt{b} < 8$.

18. Is $\sqrt{0.0625}$ a rational number? Explain.

19. The volume of a cube is 88 cubic centimeters.

   a. Approximate the side length s of the cube to the nearest whole number.

   b. Approximate the side length s of the cube to the nearest tenth.

9.6 The Converse of the Pythagorean Theorem
For use with Exploration 9.6

Learning Target: Understand the converse of the Pythagorean Theorem.

Success Criteria:
- I can explain the converse of the Pythagorean Theorem.
- I can identify right triangles given three side lengths.
- I can identify right triangles in a coordinate plane.

---

1 EXPLORATION: Analyzing the Converse of a Statement

Work with a partner.

a. Write the converse of each statement. Then determine whether each statement and its converse are *true* or *false*. Explain.

- If I live in California, then I live in the United States.

- If my heart is beating, then I am alive.

- If one figure is a translation of another figure, then the figures are congruent.

b. Write your own statement whose converse is true. Then write your own statement whose converse is false.

Big Ideas Math: Modeling Real Life Grade 7 Advanced

9.6 **The Converse of the Pythagorean Theorem** (continued)

2 **EXPLORATION:** The Converse of the Pythagorean Theorem

Work with a partner.

a. Write the converse of the Pythagorean Theorem. Do you think the converse is *true* or *false*?

b. Consider $\triangle DEF$ with side lengths a, b, and c such that $a^2 + b^2 = c^2$. Also consider $\triangle JKL$ with leg lengths a and b, where the measure of $\angle K$ is 90°. Use the two triangles and the Pythagorean Theorem to show that the converse of the Pythagorean Theorem is true.

Notetaking with Vocabulary

Vocabulary:

Notes:

 Self-Assessment

Use the scale below to rate your understanding of the learning target and the success criteria.

1	**2**	**3**	**4**
I do not understand.	I can do it with help.	I can do it on my own.	I can teach someone else.

	Rating	Date
9.6 The Converse of the Pythagorean Theorem		
Learning Target: Understand the converse of the Pythagorean Theorem.	1 2 3 4	
I can explain the converse of the Pythagorean Theorem.	1 2 3 4	
I can identify right triangles given three side lengths.	1 2 3 4	
I can identify right triangles in a coordinate plane.	1 2 3 4	

9.6 Practice

Write the converse of the statement. Then determine whether the statement and its converse are *true* or *false*. Explain.

1. If you live in New York City, then you live in New York.

2. If a is a perfect square, then $\sqrt{a}$ is an integer.

Tell whether the triangle with the given side lengths is a right triangle.

3. 11 in., 60 in., 61 in.

4. 45 cm, 26 cm, 51 cm

5. You are building an entrance sign to a resort. The entrance sign will have side lengths of 8.1 feet, 8.1 feet, and 11.5 feet. Is the sign a right triangle? Explain.

Tell whether a triangle with the given side lengths is a right triangle.

6. $9, \sqrt{54}, 8$

7. $\sqrt{704}, 27, 5$

8. 88, 103, 137

9. You are creating a flower garden in the triangular shape shown. You purchase edging to go around the flower garden. The edging costs $1.50 per foot. What is the cost of the edging? Round your lengths to the nearest whole number.

10. You and your friend are volunteering at the local preschool tricycle race. The locations of the markers for the race are represented by the points $A(0, 0), B(14, 10),$ and $C(20, -8)$. Each unit represents 1 foot.

   a. Do the three markers, A, B, and C, form a right triangle?

   b. The fastest preschooler pedals 6 feet per minute. How fast does the fastest preschooler take to pedal around the entire triangle?

   c. A preschooler accidentally moves the B marker to the $(12, 12)$ location. Do the three markers still form a right triangle? Explain.

   d. You and your friend decide to shorten the course for a running race. The course is shortened by dividing the x- and y-coordinates of the three markers by 2. What are the new points representing the markers?

   e. Do the three markers resulting from part (d) form a right triangle? Explain.

Chapter 9 Chapter Self-Assessment

Use the scale below to rate your understanding of the learning target and the success criteria.

1	2	3	4
I do not understand.	I can do it with help.	I can do it on my own.	I can teach someone else.

	Rating	Date
9.1 Finding Square Roots		
Learning Target: Understand the concept of a square root of a number.	1 2 3 4	
I can find square roots of numbers.	1 2 3 4	
I can evaluate expressions involving square roots.	1 2 3 4	
I can use square roots to solve equations.	1 2 3 4	
9.2 The Pythagorean Theorem		
Learning Target: Understand the Pythagorean Theorem.	1 2 3 4	
I can explain the Pythagorean Theorem.	1 2 3 4	
I can use the Pythagorean Theorem to find unknown side lengths of triangles.	1 2 3 4	
I can use the Pythagorean Theorem to find distances between points in a coordinate plane.	1 2 3 4	
9.3 Finding Cube Roots		
Learning Target: Understand the concept of a cube root of a number.	1 2 3 4	
I can find cube roots of numbers.	1 2 3 4	
I can evaluate expressions involving cube roots.	1 2 3 4	
I can use cube roots to solve equations.	1 2 3 4	

Chapter 9 Chapter Self-Assessment (continued)

	Rating	Date
9.4 Rational Numbers		
Learning Target: Convert between different forms of rational numbers.	1 2 3 4	
I can explain the meaning of rational numbers.	1 2 3 4	
I can write fractions and mixed numbers as decimals.	1 2 3 4	
I can write repeating decimals as fractions or mixed numbers.	1 2 3 4	
9.5 Irrational Numbers		
Learning Target: Understand the concept of irrational numbers.	1 2 3 4	
I can classify real numbers as rational or irrational.	1 2 3 4	
I can approximate irrational numbers.	1 2 3 4	
I can solve real-life problems involving irrational numbers.	1 2 3 4	
9.6 The Converse of the Pythagorean Theorem		
Learning Target: Understand the converse of the Pythagorean Theorem.	1 2 3 4	
I can explain the converse of the Pythagorean Theorem.	1 2 3 4	
I can identify right triangles given three side lengths.	1 2 3 4	
I can identify right triangles in a coordinate plane.	1 2 3 4	

Chapter 10 Review & Refresh

Find the area of the figure.

1.

2.

3.

4.

5.

6.

7. You are carpeting 2 rooms of your house. The carpet costs $1.48 per square foot. How much does it cost to carpet the rooms?

```
10 ft
12 ft
18 ft
10 ft
```

Big Ideas Math: Modeling Real Life Grade 7 Advanced **229**
Student Journal

Chapter 10 Review & Refresh (continued)

Find the area of the circle.

8.

20 in.

9.

6 m

10.

12 cm

11.

14 ft

12.

25 yd

13.

15 mm

14. Find the area of the shaded region.

3 cm

10 cm

Name_____ Date_____

Learning Target: Find the volume of a cylinder.

Success Criteria:
- I can use a formula to find the volume of a cylinder.
- I can use the formula for the volume of a cylinder to find a missing dimension.

---

1 EXPLORATION: Exploring Volume

Work with a partner.

a. Each prism shown has a height of *h* units and bases with areas of *B* square units. Write a formula that you can use to find the volume of each prism.

Triangular Prism

Rectangular Prism

Pentagonal Prism

Hexagonal Prism

Octagonal Prism

b. How can you find the volume of a prism with bases that each have 100 sides?

c. Make a conjecture about how to find the volume of a cylinder. Explain your reasoning.

10.1 Volumes of Cylinders (continued)

---

2 EXPLORATION: Finding Volume Experimentally

Work with a partner. Draw a net for a cylinder. Then cut out the net and use tape to form an open cylinder. Repeat this process to form an open cube. The edge length of the cube should be greater than the diameter and the height of the cylinder (*).

a. Use your conjecture in Exploration 1 to find the volume of the cylinder.

b. Fill the cylinder with rice. Then pour the rice into the open cube. Find the volume of rice in the cube. Does this support your answer in part (a)? Explain your reasoning.

* Nets are available in the back of the Student Journal.

Notetaking with Vocabulary

Vocabulary:

Notes:

 Self-Assessment

Use the scale below to rate your understanding of the learning target and the success criteria.

1	**2**	**3**	**4**
I do not understand.	I can do it with help.	I can do it on my own.	I can teach someone else.

	Rating	Date
10.1 Volumes of Cylinders		
Learning Target: Find the volume of a cylinder.	1 2 3 4	
I can use a formula to find the volume of a cylinder.	1 2 3 4	
I can use the formula for the volume of a cylinder to find a missing dimension.	1 2 3 4	

Name _____ Date _____

Find the volume of the cylinder. Round your answer to the nearest tenth.

1.
   9 mm
   3 mm

2.
   14 ft
   3 ft

3. A cylinder has a surface are of 748 cm² and a radius of 7 cm. Estimate the volume of the cylinder to the nearest whole number.

4. A cylinder has a volume of 100π cubic meters.

   a. What is the volume of the cylinder if the height is halved? Explain.

   b. What is the volume of the cylinder if the diameter is halved? Explain.

Find the missing dimension of the cylinder. Round your answer to the nearest whole number.

5. Volume = 550 in.³

   10 in.
   h

6. Volume = 25,000 ft³

   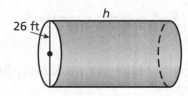
   h
   26 ft

7. Your friend's swimming pool is in the shape of a rectangular prism, with a length of 25 feet, a width of 8 feet, and a height of 5 feet.

   a. What is the volume of your friend's swimming pool?

   b. Your swimming pool is in the shape of a cylinder with a diameter of 16 feet and has the same volume as your friend's pool. What is the height of your pool? Round your answer to the nearest whole number.

   c. While you were on vacation, 6 inches of water evaporated from your pool. About how many gallons of water evaporated from your pool? (1 ft³ ≈ 7.5 gal) Round your answer to the nearest whole number.

10.2 Volumes of Cones
For use with Exploration 10.2

Learning Target: Find the volume of a cone.

Success Criteria:
- I can use a formula to find the volume of a cone.
- I can use the formula for the volume of a cone to find a missing dimension.

---

1 EXPLORATION: Finding a Formula Experimentally

Work with a partner. Use a paper cup that is shaped like a cone. Measure the height of the cup and the diameter of the circular base. Use these measurements to draw a net for a cylinder with the same base and height as the paper cup. Then cut out the net and use tape to form an open cylinder (*).

   a. Find the volume of the cylinder.

   b. Fill the paper cup with rice. Then pour the rice into the cylinder. Repeat this until the cylinder is full. How many cones does it take to fill the cylinder?

   * Nets are available in the back of the Student Journal.

10.2 **Volumes of Cones** (continued)

c. Use your result to write a formula for the volume of a cone.

d. Use your formula in part (c) to find the volume of the cone. How can you tell whether your answer is correct?

e. Do you think your formula for the volume of a cone is also true for *oblique* cones? Explain your reasoning.

10.2 Notetaking with Vocabulary

Vocabulary:

Notes:

10.2 Self-Assessment

Use the scale below to rate your understanding of the learning target and the success criteria.

1	2	3	4
I do not understand.	I can do it with help.	I can do it on my own.	I can teach someone else.

	Rating	Date
10.2 Volumes of Cones		
Learning Target: Find the volume of a cone.	1 2 3 4	
I can use a formula to find the volume of a cone.	1 2 3 4	
I can use the formula for the volume of a cone to find a missing dimension.	1 2 3 4	

Name _____ Date _____

10.2 Practice

Find the volume of the cone. Round your answer to the nearest tenth.

1.
10 mm
8 mm

2.
7 ft
12 ft

3. The volume of a cylinder is twice the volume of a cone. The cone and the cylinder have the same diameter. The height of the cylinder is 5 meters. What is the height of the cone?

4. One package of popcorn makes 1000 cubic inches of popcorn. The movie theatre sells the popcorn in cone shaped containers. The containers have a radius of 3 inches and a height of 8 inches. How many containers can the movie theatre fill from one package of popcorn?

Find the missing dimension of the cone. Round your answer to the nearest tenth.

5. Volume = 100 in.^{3}

h
8 in.

6. Volume = 13.4 m^3

h
3.2 m

7. A paper cup is in the shape of a cone, with a diameter of 2 centimeters and a height of 5 centimeters.

   a. What is the volume of the paper cup?

   b. Water is running into the cup at a rate of 1.5 cubic centimeters per second. How long does it take for the cup to fill with water? Round your answer to the nearest tenth.

8. Cone A has the same radius but half the height of Cone B. What is the ratio of the volume of Cone A to the volume of Cone B?

10.3 Volumes of Spheres
For use with Exploration 10.3

Learning Target: Find the volume of a sphere.

Success Criteria:
- I can use a formula to find the volume of a sphere.
- I can use the formula for the volume of a sphere to find the radius.
- I can find volumes of composite solids.

---

1 EXPLORATION: Finding a Formula Experimentally

Work with a partner. Use a plastic ball similar to the one shown. Draw a net for a cylinder with a diameter and a height equal to the diameter of the ball. Then cut out the net and use tape to form an open cylinder.

a. How is the height h of the cylinder related to the radius r of the ball?

10.3 **Volumes of Spheres** (continued)

b. Cover the ball with aluminum foil or tape. Leave one hole open. Fill the ball with rice. Then pour the rice into the cylinder. What fraction of the cylinder is filled with the rice?

c. Use your result in part (b) and the formula for the volume of a cylinder to write a formula for the volume of a sphere. Explain your reasoning.

10.3 Notetaking with Vocabulary

Vocabulary:

Notes:

10.3 Self-Assessment

Use the scale below to rate your understanding of the learning target and the success criteria.

1	**2**	**3**	**4**
I do not understand.	I can do it with help.	I can do it on my own.	I can teach someone else.

	Rating	Date
10.3 Volumes of Spheres		
Learning Target: Find the volume of a sphere.	1 2 3 4	
I can use a formula to find the volume of a sphere.	1 2 3 4	
I can use the formula for the volume of a sphere to find the radius.	1 2 3 4	
I can find volumes of composite solids.	1 2 3 4	

10.3 Practice

Find the volume of the sphere. Round your answer to the nearest tenth.

1.

14 m

2.

4.5 mi

3. A cylinder and a sphere have the same radius and volume. The height of the cylinder is 12 cm. What is the volume of the sphere rounded to the nearest whole number?

4. You want to give your friend a soccer ball for a gift. The soccer ball has a volume of 85.3π cubic inches. What is the volume of the smallest cube shaped box that will fit inside?

Find the radius of a sphere with the given volume. Round your answer to the nearest tenth if necessary.

5. Volume = 2304π yd^3

6. Volume = 1543.5π yd^3

7. A spherical cabinet knob has a radius of 1.5 inches. Find the volume of the cabinet knob. Round your answer to the nearest tenth.

Find the volume of the composite solid. Round your answer to the nearest tenth.

8.

5 ft

5 ft

9.

9 m

6 m

10. Rubber balls are packaged in a box with dimensions 8.5 cm, 5 cm, 5 cm. Each ball has a diameter of 3 cm. If there are a dozen balls in the box, how much space in the box is not occupied by the rubber balls? Round your answer to the nearest tenth.

Name_____ Date _____

Learning Target: Find the surface areas and volumes of similar solids.

Success Criteria:
- I can use corresponding dimensions to determine whether solids are similar.
- I can use corresponding dimensions to find missing measures in similar solids.
- I can use linear measures to find surface areas and volumes of similar solids.

1 EXPLORATION: Comparing Similar Solids

Work with a partner.

a. You multiply the dimensions of the smallest cylinder by different factors to create the other four cylinders. Complete the table. Compare the surface area and volume of each cylinder with the surface area and volume of the smallest cylinder.

Radius	1	2	3	4	5
Height	1	2	3	4	5
Surface Area					
Volume					

10.4 **Surface Areas and Volumes of Similar Solids** (continued)

b. Repeat part (a) using the square pyramids and table below.

Base Side	6	12	18	24	30
Height	4	8	12	16	20
Slant Height	5	10	15	20	25
Surface Area					
Volume					

Name_____ Date_____

 Notetaking with Vocabulary

Vocabulary:

Notes:

10.4 **Self-Assessment**

Use the scale below to rate your understanding of the learning target and
the success criteria.

1	**2**	**3**	**4**
I do not understand.	I can do it with help.	I can do it on my own.	I can teach someone else.

	Rating	Date
10.4 Surface Areas and Volumes of Similar Solids		
Learning Target: Find the surface areas and volumes of similar solids.	1 2 3 4	
I can use corresponding dimensions to determine whether solids are similar.	1 2 3 4	
I can use corresponding dimensions to find missing measures in similar solids.	1 2 3 4	
I can use linear measures to find surface areas and volumes of similar solids.	1 2 3 4	

Name _____ Date _____

The solids are similar. Find the missing measure(s).

1.

2.

The solids are similar. Find the surface area S or the volume V of the smaller solid. Round your answers to the nearest tenth.

3. Surface Area = 294.7 m²

4. Volume = 1500 ft³

5. The ratio of the corresponding linear measures of two similar buckets of popcorn is 2 to 5. The larger bucket has a volume of 390 cubic inches. Find the volume of the smaller bucket. Round your answer to the nearest tenth.

6. A box of 60 tissues has a length of 11 centimeters, a width of 10.5 centimeters, and a height of 13.5 centimeters.

   a. Find the volume of the box of tissues. Round your answer to the nearest tenth.

   b. A similar box contains 100 tissues. The ratio of the corresponding linear measures of the two boxes is 3 : 5. Find the volume of the larger box. Round your answer to the nearest tenth.

   c. Find the dimensions of the larger box. Round your answers to the nearest tenth.

Name_____ Date_____

Use the scale below to rate your understanding of the learning target and the success criteria.

1	2	3	4
I do not understand.	I can do it with help.	I can do it on my own.	I can teach someone else.

	Rating	Date
10.1 Volumes of Cylinders		
Learning Target: Find the volume of a cylinder.	1 2 3 4	
I can use a formula to find the volume of a cylinder.	1 2 3 4	
I can use the formula for the volume of a cylinder to find a missing dimension.	1 2 3 4	
10.2 Volumes of Cones		
Learning Target: Find the volume of a cone.	1 2 3 4	
I can use a formula to find the volume of a cone.	1 2 3 4	
I can use the formula for the volume of a cone to find a missing dimension.	1 2 3 4	
10.3 Volumes of Spheres		
Learning Target: Find the volume of a sphere.	1 2 3 4	
I can use a formula to find the volume of a sphere.	1 2 3 4	
I can use the formula for the volume of a sphere to find the radius.	1 2 3 4	
I can find volumes of composite solids.	1 2 3 4	

Chapter 10 Chapter Self-Assessment (continued)

	Rating	Date
10.4 Surface Areas and Volumes of Similar Solids		
Learning Target: Find the surface areas and volumes of similar solids.	1 2 3 4	
I can use corresponding dimensions to determine whether solids are similar.	1 2 3 4	
I can use corresponding dimensions to find missing measures in similar solids.	1 2 3 4	
I can use linear measures to find surface areas and volumes of similar solids.	1 2 3 4	

Review & Refresh

Write the phrase as an algebraic expression.

1. the sum of eight and a number y

2. six less than a number p

3. the product of seven and a number m

4. eight less than the product of eleven and a number c

5. a number r decreased by the quotient of a number r and two

6. the product of nine and the sum of a number z and four

Chapter A Review & Refresh (continued)

Complete the number sentence with < or >.

7. $\frac{3}{4}$ ___ 0.2

8. $\frac{7}{8}$ ___ 0.7

9. -0.6 ___ $-\frac{2}{3}$

10. -1.76 ___ 1.75

11. $\frac{17}{3}$ ___ 6

12. 1.8 ___ $\frac{31}{16}$

13. Your height is 5 feet and $1\frac{5}{8}$ inches. Your friend's height is 5.6 feet. Who is taller? Explain.

A.1 Solving Equations Using Addition or Subtraction
For use with Exploration A.1

Learning Target: Write and solve equations using addition or subtraction.

Success Criteria:
- I can apply the Addition and Subtraction Properties of Equality to produce equivalent equations.
- I can solve equations using addition or subtraction.
- I can apply equations involving addition or subtraction to solve real-life problems.

---

1 EXPLORATION: Using Algebra Tiles to Solve Equations

Work with a partner.

a. Use the examples to explain the meaning of each property.

Addition Property of Equality: $x + 2 = 1$

$$x + 2 + 5 = 1 + 5$$

Subtraction Property of Equality: $x + 2 = 1$

$$x + 2 - 1 = 1 - 1$$

Are these properties true for equations involving negative numbers? Explain your reasoning.

A.1 **Solving Equations Using Addition or Subtraction** (continued)

b. Write the four equations modeled by the algebra tiles. Explain how you can use algebra tiles to solve each equation. Then find the solutions.

$$\boxed{+}\ \boxed{-}\ \boxed{-}\ \boxed{-} \;=\; \boxed{+}\ \boxed{+}\ \boxed{+}\ \boxed{+}$$

$$\boxed{-}\ \boxed{-}\ \boxed{-}\ \boxed{-}\ \boxed{-} \;=\; \boxed{+}\ \boxed{+}\ \boxed{+}$$

$$\boxed{+}\ \boxed{-}\ \boxed{-}\ \boxed{-} \;=\; \boxed{+}\ \boxed{+}\ \boxed{+}$$

$$\boxed{+}\ \boxed{+}\ \boxed{+}\ \boxed{+}\ \boxed{+} \;=\; \boxed{+}\ \boxed{-}\ \boxed{-}$$

c. How can you solve each equation in part (b) without using algebra tiles?

Notetaking with Vocabulary

Vocabulary:

Notes:

Self-Assessment

Use the scale below to rate your understanding of the learning target and the success criteria.

1	2	3	4
I do not understand.	I can do it with help.	I can do it on my own.	I can teach someone else.

	Rating	Date
A.1 Solving Equations Using Addition or Subtraction		
Learning Target: Write and solve equations using addition or subtraction.	1 2 3 4	
I can apply the Addition and Subtraction Properties of Equality to produce equivalent equations.	1 2 3 4	
I can solve equations using addition or subtraction.	1 2 3 4	
I can apply equations involving addition or subtraction to solve real-life problems.	1 2 3 4	

A.1 Practice

Solve the equation. Check your solution.

1. $-4.5 = m + 1.9$

2. $10\frac{2}{3} = r + 12\frac{1}{6}$

3. $b + 4.006 = 9$

4. $-7\frac{5}{8} = 1\frac{5}{6} + d$

5. $f - \frac{2}{15} = 6\frac{3}{5}$

6. $-10.216 + c = -12.014$

Write the word sentence as an equation. Then solve the equation.

7. 27 is 12 more than a number x.

8. The difference of a number p and -9 is 12.

9. 35 less than a number m is -72.

10. You swim the 50-meter freestyle in 28.12 seconds. This is 0.14 second less than your previous fastest time. Write and solve an equation to find your previous fastest time.

11. The perimeter of a rectangular backyard is $32\frac{1}{2}$ meters. The two shorter sides are each $7\frac{3}{8}$ meters long. Write and solve an equation to find the length of the two longer sides? (*Hint:* The sum of the shorter side and the longer side is equal to half of the perimeter.)

12. The wind chill when the airplane lands in Minneapolis is $-70.2°F$, which is $140.8°F$ less than the wind chill when the airplane took off in Orlando. Write and solve an equation to find the wind chill when the airplane took off in Orlando.

13. Your cell phone bill in August was $61.43, which was $21.75 more than your bill in July. Your cell phone bill in July was $13.62 less than your bill in June. What was your cell phone bill in June?

Solve the equation.

14. $|x| - 10.5 = 4.3$

15. $|x + 2| - 7 = 5$

16. Find the value of $3x + 2$ when $x - 5 = -8$.

17. Find the values of $x - 4$ when $|x| + 1 = 3$.

Solving Equations Using Multiplication or Division
For use with Exploration A.2

Learning Target: Write and solve equations using multiplication or division.

Success Criteria:
- I can apply the Multiplication and Division Properties of Equality to produce equivalent equations.
- I can solve equations using multiplication or division.
- I can apply equations involving multiplication or division to solve real-life problems.

---

1 EXPLORATION: Using Algebra Tiles to Solve Equations

Work with a partner.

    a. Use the examples to explain the meaning of each property.

Multiplication Property of Equality: $\qquad 3x = 1$

$$2 \cdot 3x = 2 \cdot 1$$

Division Property of Equality: $\qquad 3x = 1$

$$\frac{3x}{4} = \frac{1}{4}$$

Are these properties true for equations involving negative numbers?
Explain your reasoning.

Big Ideas Math: Modeling Real Life Grade 7 Advanced **255**
Student Journal

A.2 **Solving Equations Using Multiplication or Division** (continued)

b. Write the three equations modeled by the algebra tiles. Explain how you can use algebra tiles to solve each equation. Then find the solutions.

c. How can you solve each equation in part (b) without using algebra tiles?

Notetaking with Vocabulary

Vocabulary:

Notes:

 Self-Assessment

Use the scale below to rate your understanding of the learning target and the success criteria.

1	2	3	4
I do not understand.	I can do it with help.	I can do it on my own.	I can teach someone else.

	Rating	Date
A.2 Solving Equations Using Multiplication or Division		
Learning Target: Write and solve equations using multiplication or division.	1 2 3 4	
I can apply the Multiplication and Division Properties of Equality to produce equivalent equations.	1 2 3 4	
I can solve equations using multiplication or division.	1 2 3 4	
I can apply equations involving multiplication or division to solve real-life problems.	1 2 3 4	

A.2 Practice

Solve the equation. Check your solution.

1. $-14p = -21$

2. $-\dfrac{8}{15}k = -4$

3. $-7.24q = 17.014$

4. $\dfrac{g}{0.003} = -2.8$

5. $-\dfrac{10}{21}c = -\dfrac{15}{28}$

6. $18 = -\dfrac{6}{11}h$

7. You order an entrée for \$12.00. You pay \$0.78 in taxes. Write and solve an equation to determine the tax rate.

8. If a project is handed in late, you receive $\dfrac{8}{9}$ of your earned points. You received 72 points on your late project. Write and solve an equation to determine how many points you lost.

9. Write a multiplication equation that has a solution of -14.8.

10. Write a division equation that has a solution of $-\dfrac{9}{14}$.

Write the word sentence as an equation. Then solve the equation.

11. A number divided by $\dfrac{1}{2}$ is 10.

12. The product of a number and -12 is -8.

13. The quotient of 9.75 and a number is -6.5

14. There are 92 students in a room. They are separated into 18 groups. How many students are in each group? How many students are not in a group?

15. A bus token costs \$1.75.

   a. You spend \$15.75 on tokens. Write and solve an equation to find how many tokens you purchase.

   b. If you purchase 10 tokens, you get 2 free tokens. Write and solve an equation to find the approximate reduced price of each token when purchasing this special.

   c. You also receive free tokens if you purchase 20 tokens. The reduced price for each token is \$1.40. Write and solve an equation to find how many free tokens you receive when purchasing this special.

16. Solve $\dfrac{1}{3}|z| = 2$.

A.3 Solving Two-Step Equations
For use with Exploration A.3

Learning Target: Write and solve two-step equations.

Success Criteria:
- I can apply properties of equality to produce equivalent equations.
- I can solve two-step equations using the basic operations.
- I can apply two-step equations to solve real-life problems.

---

1 EXPLORATION: Using Algebra Tiles to Solve Equations

Work with a partner.

a. What is being modeled by the algebra tiles below? What is the solution?

b. Use properties of equality to solve the original equation in part (a). How do your steps compare to the steps performed with algebra tiles?

A.3 **Solving Two-Step Equations** (continued)

c. Write the three equations modeled by the algebra tiles below. Then solve each equation using algebra tiles. Check your answers using properties of equality.

d. Explain how to solve an equation of the form $ax + b = c$ for x.

Name_____ Date_____

 A.3 **Notetaking with Vocabulary**

Vocabulary:

Notes:

A.3 **Self-Assessment**

Use the scale below to rate your understanding of the learning target and the success criteria.

1	**2**	**3**	**4**
I do not understand.	I can do it with help.	I can do it on my own.	I can teach someone else.

	Rating	Date
A.3 Solving Two-Step Equations		
Learning Target: Write and solve two-step equations.	1 2 3 4	
I can apply properties of equality to produce equivalent equations.	1 2 3 4	
I can solve two-step equations using the basic operations.	1 2 3 4	
I can apply two-step equations to solve real-life problems.	1 2 3 4	

Name _____ Date _____

A.3 Practice

Solve the equation. Check your solution.

1. $25 = 4.5z + 12$

2. $5.25s - 2.01 = -8.94$

3. $16 + 2.4c = 22.5$

4. $4h + \frac{1}{3} = \frac{3}{4}$

5. $\frac{1}{7}f - 5\frac{1}{2} = \frac{9}{14}$

6. $-\frac{1}{2}u + \frac{3}{5} = \frac{1}{6}$

7. You purchased $132.49 worth of wheels and bearings for your skateboards. The shop charges $15 per board to install them. The total cost is $192.49. Write and solve an equation to determine how many skateboards will be repaired.

8. A music download service charges a flat fee each month and $0.99 per download. The total cost for downloading 27 songs this month is $42.72. Write and solve an equation to determine the flat fee.

Solve the equation. Check your solution.

9. $-5(m + 4) = 27$

10. $-12(a - 2) = -50$

11. $-5x - 2x + 3x = 9$

12. The perimeter of a triangle is 60 feet. One leg is 12 feet long. Of the two unknown sides, one the them is twice as long as the other. Find the lengths of the two unknown sides.

13. Sally picks seashells by the seashore. She lost 17 of them on her way home. With the remaining seashells, she planned to fill 5 jars with the same number of seashells in each. How many seashells did Sally originally pick?

   a. You do not have enough information to solve this problem. The number of seashells in each jar is the same as the number portion of her street address, which is a 2-digit number. The first digit is 5. The last digit is 9 less than 3 times the first digit. How many seashells did Sally plan to put in each jar?

   b. By working backwards, determine how many seashells Sally originally picked.

   c. The 5 jars that Sally chose would not each hold that many seashells. In her search for a 6th jar, she discovered a few seashells in her pocket. What are possible values for the number of seashells in each of the 6 jars and the number of seashells discovered in her pocket, such that there are no seashells left over?

Writing and Graphing Inequalities
For use with Exploration A.4

Learning Target: Write inequalities and represent solutions of inequalities on number lines.

Success Criteria:
- I can write word sentences as inequalities.
- I can determine whether a value is a solution of an inequality.
- I can graph the solutions of inequalities.

---

1 EXPLORATION: Understanding Inequality Statements

Work with a partner. Create a number line on the floor with both positive and negative numbers.

a. For each statement, stand at a number on your number line that could represent the situation. On what other numbers can you stand?

At least 3 students from our school are in a chess tournament.

Your ring size is less than 7.5.

The temperature is no more than −1 degree Fahrenheit.

A.4 Writing and Graphing Inequalities (continued)

The elevation of a frogfish is greater than $-8\frac{1}{2}$ meters.

b. How can you represent all of the solutions for each statement in part (a) on a number line?

Name_____ Date_____

 Notetaking with Vocabulary

Vocabulary:

Notes:

 Self-Assessment

Use the scale below to rate your understanding of the learning target and the success criteria.

1	2	3	4
I do not understand.	I can do it with help.	I can do it on my own.	I can teach someone else.

	Rating	Date
A.4 Writing and Graphing Inequalities		
Learning Target: Write inequalities and represent solutions of inequalities on number lines.	1 2 3 4	
I can write word sentences as inequalities.	1 2 3 4	
I can determine whether a value is a solution of an inequality.	1 2 3 4	
I can graph the solutions of inequalities.	1 2 3 4	

A.4 Practice

Write an inequality for the graph. Then, in words, describe all the values of x that make the inequality true.

1.

2.

Write the word sentence as an inequality.

3. A number x is at least 15.

4. A number r added to 3.7 is less than 1.2.

5. A number h divided by 2 is more than -5.

6. A number a minus 8.2 is no greater than 12.

Tell whether the given value is a solution of the inequality.

7. $p + 1.7 \geq -4; p = -9$

8. $\frac{3}{4} - d > \frac{1}{3}; d = \frac{1}{2}$

9. $5t < 4 - t; t = -3$

10. $\frac{q}{5} < q - 20; q = 15$

Graph the inequality on a number line.

11. $\ell \leq 3.5$

12. $m > -15$

13. To get a job at the local restaurant, you must be at least 16 years old. Write an inequality that represents this situation.

14. In order to qualify for a college scholarship, you must have acceptable scores in either the SAT or the ACT along with the following requirements: a minimum GPA of 3.5; at least 12 credits of college preparatory academic courses; and at least 75 hours of community service.

   a. Write and graph three inequalities that represent the requirements.

   b. Your cousin has a GPA of 3.6, 15 credits of college preparatory class, and 65 hours of community service. Other than the test scores, does your cousin satisfy the requirements? Explain.

15. Which of the following is not equivalent? Explain.

   A number x is at most 3.

   A number x is not greater than 3.

   A number x is less than 3.

   A number x is less than or equal to 3.

Name_____ Date_____

Learning Target: Write and solve inequalities using addition or subtraction.

Success Criteria:
- I can apply the Addition and Subtraction Properties of Inequality to produce equivalent inequalities.
- I can solve inequalities using addition or subtraction.
- I can apply inequalities involving addition or subtraction to solve real-life problems.

---

1   EXPLORATION: Writing Inequalities

Work with a partner. Use two number cubes on which the odd numbers are negative on one of the number cubes and the even numbers are negative on the other number cube.

Roll the number cubes. Write an inequality that compares the numbers.

Roll one of the number cubes. Add the number to each side of the inequality and record your result.

Repeat the previous two steps five more times.

A.5 **Solving Inequalities Using Addition or Subtraction** (continued)

a. When you add the same number to each side of an inequality, does the inequality remain true? Explain your reasoning.

b. When you subtract the same number from each side of an inequality, does the inequality remain true? Use inequalities generated by number cubes to justify your answer.

c. Use your results in parts (a) and (b) to make a conjecture about how to solve an inequality of the form $x + a < b$ for x.

Notetaking with Vocabulary

Vocabulary:

Notes:

 Self-Assessment

Use the scale below to rate your understanding of the learning target and the success criteria.

1	2	3	4
I do not understand.	I can do it with help.	I can do it on my own.	I can teach someone else.

	Rating	Date
A.5 Solving Inequalities Using Addition or Subtraction		
Learning Target: Write and solve inequalities using addition or subtraction.	1 2 3 4	
I can apply the Addition and Subtraction Properties of Inequality to produce equivalent inequalities.	1 2 3 4	
I can solve inequalities using addition or subtraction.	1 2 3 4	
I can apply inequalities involving addition or subtraction to solve real-life problems.	1 2 3 4	

Big Ideas Math: Modeling Real Life Grade 7 Advanced **269**
Student Journal

A.5 Practice

Solve the inequality. Graph the solution.

1. $w - 1.8 < 2.5$

2. $v + \frac{1}{3} > 8$

3. $\frac{2}{5} < \frac{4}{5} + k$

4. $q + \frac{3}{4} \geq -\frac{1}{4}$

5. $7.4 > c + 3.9$

6. $p - 10.2 > 3.5$

7. You and two friends are diving for lobster. The maximum number of lobsters you may have on your boat is 18. You currently have 7 lobsters.

   a. Write and solve an inequality that represents the additional lobsters that you may catch.

   b. Another friend comes on your boat and he has 3 lobsters. You may now have 24 lobsters on your boat. Write and solve an inequality that represents the additional lobsters that you may catch.

   c. How many lobsters is each person allowed to catch?

Write and solve an inequality that represents x.

8. The length is greater than the width.

8 m

$x - 4$

9. The perimeter is less than or equal to 50 inches.

8 in.

8 in.

$x + 4$

5 in.

5 in.

5 in.

10. The solution of $w - c > -3.4$ is $w > -1.4$. What is the value of c?

11. Describe all numbers that are solutions to $|x| < 5$.

12. The *triangle inequality theorem* states that the sum of the lengths of any two sides of a triangle is greater than the length of the third side. A triangle has side lengths of 6 inches and 17 inches. What are the possible values for the length of the third side? Explain how you found your answer.

13. The possible values of x are given by $x - 5 \geq 7$. What is the least possible value of $9x$? Explain your reasoning.

A.6 Solving Inequalities Using Multiplication or Division
For use with Exploration A.6

Learning Target: Write and solve inequalities using multiplication or division.

Success Criteria:
- I can apply the Multiplication and Division Properties of Inequality to produce equivalent inequalities.
- I can solve inequalities using multiplication or division.
- I can apply inequalities involving multiplication or division to solve real-life problems.

---

1 EXPLORATION: Writing Inequalities

Work with a partner. Use two number cubes on which the odd numbers are negative on one of the number cubes and the even numbers are negative on the other number cube.

Roll the number cubes. Write an inequality that compares the numbers.

Roll one of the number cubes. Multiply each side of the inequality by the number and record your result.

Repeat the previous two steps nine more times.

A.6 **Solving Inequalities Using Multiplication or Division** (continued)

a. When you multiply each side of an inequality by the same number, does the inequality remain true? Explain your reasoning?

b. When you divide each side of an inequality by the same number, does the inequality remain true? Use inequalities generated by number cubes to justify your answer.

c. Use your results in parts (a) and (b) to make a conjecture about how to solve an inequality of the form $ax < b$ for x when $a > 0$ and when $a < 0$.

A.6 Notetaking with Vocabulary

Vocabulary:

Notes:

A.6 Self-Assessment

Use the scale below to rate your understanding of the learning target and the success criteria.

1	*2*	*3*	*4*
I do not understand.	I can do it with help.	I can do it on my own.	I can teach someone else.

	Rating	Date
A.6 Solving Inequalities Using Multiplication or Division		
Learning Target: Write and solve inequalities using multiplication or division.	1 2 3 4	
I can apply the Multiplication and Division Properties of Inequality to produce equivalent inequalities.	1 2 3 4	
I can solve inequalities using multiplication or division.	1 2 3 4	
I can apply inequalities involving multiplication or division to solve real-life problems.	1 2 3 4	

A.6 Practice

Solve the inequality. Graph the solution.

1. $3y \leq \frac{3}{4}$

2. $\frac{s}{3.1} \geq 4.5$

3. $-\frac{4}{5} < 2x$

4. $-\frac{d}{2} > \frac{3}{8}$

5. $-1.2 \leq -0.8r$

6. $\frac{j}{-5.2} \leq -1.5$

Write the word sentence as an inequality. Then solve the inequality.

7. A number divided by 5 is at least 4.

8. The product of 2 and a number is at most −6.

9. The solution of $cx \geq -4$ is $x \geq -8$. What is the value of c?

10. The height of a room is 10 feet. You are building shelving from the floor to the ceiling.

   a. Each shelf requires 8 inches. Write and solve an inequality that represents the number of shelves that can be made.

   b. You forgot to include the thickness of each shelf in your measurements. The amount of space needed for each shelf is actually 10 inches. Write and solve an inequality that represents the number of shelves that can be made.

11. Students in a math class are divided into 8 equal groups with at least 3 students in each group for a project.

   a. Write an inequality to describe the possible numbers of students in each group.

   b. Use the Multiplication Property of Inequality to write an inequality to describe the possible numbers of students in the class.

Describe all numbers that satisfy *both* inequalities. Include a graph with your description.

12. $-3x < -9$ and $-3x < 9$

13. $\frac{2}{3}t \geq 4$ and $-\frac{3}{5}t \geq -6$

14. $3x < 12$ and $-3x < -3$

15. $\frac{y}{5} \leq -2$ and $-\frac{y}{4} \geq 1$

A.7 Solving Two-Step Inequalities
For use with Exploration A.7

Learning Target: Write and solve two-step inequalities.

Success Criteria:
- I can apply properties of inequality to generate equivalent inequalities.
- I can solve two-step inequalities using the basic operations.
- I can apply two-step inequalities to solve real-life problems.

---

1 EXPLORATION: Using Algebra Tiles to Solve Inequalities

Work with a partner.

a. What is being modeled by the algebra tiles below? What is the solution?

b. Use properties of inequality to solve the original inequality in part (a). How do your steps compare to the steps performed with algebra tiles?

Big Ideas Math: Modeling Real Life Grade 7 Advanced **275**
Student Journal

A.7 **Solving Two-Step Inequalities** (continued)

c. Write the three inequalities modeled by the algebra tiles below. Then solve each inequality using algebra tiles. Check your answer using properties of inequality.

d. Explain how solving a two-step inequality is similar to solving a two-step equation.

Name_____ Date_____

 Notetaking with Vocabulary

Vocabulary:

Notes:

A.7 Self-Assessment

Use the scale below to rate your understanding of the learning target and the success criteria.

1	**2**	**3**	**4**
I do not understand.	I can do it with help.	I can do it on my own.	I can teach someone else.

	Rating	Date
A.7 Solving Two-Step Inequalities		
Learning Target: Write and solve two-step inequalities.	1 2 3 4	
I can apply properties of inequality to generate equivalent inequalities.	1 2 3 4	
I can solve two-step inequalities using the basic operations.	1 2 3 4	
I can apply two-step inequalities to solve real-life problems.	1 2 3 4	

A.7 Practice

Solve the inequality. Graph the solution.

1. $2 - \dfrac{q}{3} > 6$

2. $7 \leq 0.5v + 10$

3. $-5(m - 2) > 30$

4. $-\dfrac{3}{2}(f + 6) \leq -6$

5. $10.5 < 1.5(p - 3)$

6. $30 \geq -7.5(w - 4.2)$

7. An RV park receives \$300 per month from each residential site that is occupied as well as \$2000 per month from their overnight sites. Write and solve an inequality to find the number of residential sites that must be occupied to make at least \$14,000 in revenue each month.

8. Write and solve an inequality that represents the values of x for which the area of the rectangle will be at most 45 square meters.

4.5 m

$x + 3$

Solve the inequality. Graph the solution.

9. $12x - 5x - 4 \geq 60 - 8$

10. $4v + 6v + 3.2 < 6.8 - 9.2$

11. An animal shelter has fixed weekly expenses of \$750. Each animal in the shelter costs an additional \$6 a week.

    a. During the summer months, the total weekly expenses are at least \$1170. Write and solve an inequality that represents the number of animals at the shelter for expenses to be at least \$1170 a week.

    b. During the winter months, the total weekly expenses are at most \$900. Write and solve an inequality that represents the number of animals at the shelter for expenses to be at most \$900 a week.

    c. The cost for each animal has increased by \$2. What will be the maximum weekly expenses during the winter month?

12. For what values of r will the area of the shaded region be greater than or equal to half of the area of the larger rectangle?

6 8

r

12

Name_____ Date_____

Chapter Self-Assessment

Use the scale below to rate your understanding of the learning target and the success criteria.

1	**2**	**3**	**4**
I do not understand.	I can do it with help.	I can do it on my own.	I can teach someone else.

	Rating	Date
A.1 Solving Equations Using Addition or Subtraction		
Learning Target: Write and solve equations using addition or subtraction.	1 2 3 4	
I can apply the Addition and Subtraction Properties of Equality to produce equivalent equations.	1 2 3 4	
I can solve equations using addition or subtraction.	1 2 3 4	
I can apply equations involving addition or subtraction to solve real-life problems.	1 2 3 4	
A.2 Solving Equations Using Multiplication or Division		
Learning Target: Write and solve equations using multiplication or division.	1 2 3 4	
I can apply the Multiplication and Division Properties of Equality to produce equivalent equations.	1 2 3 4	
I can solve equations using multiplication or division.	1 2 3 4	
I can apply equations involving multiplication or division to solve real-life problems.	1 2 3 4	
A.3 Solving Two-Step Equations		
Learning Target: Write and solve two-step equations.	1 2 3 4	
I can apply properties of equality to produce equivalent equations.	1 2 3 4	
I can solve two-step equations using the basic operations.	1 2 3 4	
I can apply two-step equations to solve real-life problems.	1 2 3 4	

Chapter A — Chapter Self-Assessment (continued)

	Rating	Date
A.4 Writing and Graphing Inequalities		
Learning Target: Write inequalities and represent solutions of inequalities on number lines.	1 2 3 4	
I can write word sentences as inequalities.	1 2 3 4	
I can determine whether a value is a solution of an inequality.	1 2 3 4	
I can graph the solutions of inequalities.	1 2 3 4	
A.5 Solving Inequalities Using Addition or Subtraction		
Learning Target: Write and solve inequalities using addition or subtraction.	1 2 3 4	
I can apply the Addition and Subtraction Properties of Inequality to produce equivalent inequalities.	1 2 3 4	
I can solve inequalities using addition or subtraction.	1 2 3 4	
I can apply inequalities involving addition or subtraction to solve real-life problems.	1 2 3 4	
A.6 Solving Inequalities Using Multiplication or Division		
Learning Target: Write and solve inequalities using multiplication or division.	1 2 3 4	
I can apply the Multiplication and Division Properties of Inequality to produce equivalent inequalities.	1 2 3 4	
I can solve inequalities using multiplication or division.	1 2 3 4	
I can apply inequalities involving multiplication or division to solve real-life problems.	1 2 3 4	
A.7 Solving Two-Step Inequalities		
Learning Target: Write and solve two-step inequalities.	1 2 3 4	
I can apply properties of inequality to generate equivalent inequalities.	1 2 3 4	
I can solve two-step inequalities using the basic operations.	1 2 3 4	
I can apply two-step inequalities to solve real-life problems.	1 2 3 4	

Chapter B Review & Refresh

Write the ratio in simplest form.

1. bats to baseballs

2. bows to gift boxes

3. hammers to screwdrivers

4. apples to bananas

5. There are 100 students in the sixth grade. There are 15 sixth-grade teachers. What is the ratio of teachers to students?

Chapter B **Review & Refresh** (continued)

Write the ratio in simplest form.

6. golf balls to total number of balls

7. rulers to total pieces of equipment

8. apples to total number of fruit

9. small fish to total number of fish

10. There are 24 flute players and 18 trumpet players in the band. Write the ratio of trumpet players to total number of trumpet players and flute players.

B.1　Probability
For use with Exploration B.1

Learning Target:　Understand how the probability of an event indicates its likelihood.

Success Criteria:
- I can identify possible outcomes of an experiment.
- I can use probability and relative frequency to describe the likelihood of an event.
- I can use relative frequency to make predictions.

1　EXPLORATION: Determining Likelihood

Work with a partner. Use the spinners shown.

a. For each spinner, determine which numbers you are more likely to spin and which numbers you are less likely to spin. Explain your reasoning.

　Big Ideas Math: Modeling Real Life Grade 7 Advanced　**283**
Student Journal

B.1 **Probability** (continued)

b. Spin each spinner 20 times (*) and record your results in two tables. Do the data support your answers in part (a)? Explain why or why not?

Spinner 1	
Number	**Frequency**
1	
2	
3	
4	
5	
6	

Spinner 2	
Number	**Frequency**
1	
2	
3	
4	
5	
6	

c. How can you use percents to describe the likelihood of spinning each number? Explain.

(*) Spinners are available in the back of the Student Journal.

B.1 Notetaking with Vocabulary

Vocabulary:

Notes:

B.1 Self-Assessment

Use the scale below to rate your understanding of the learning target and the success criteria.

1	2	3	4
I do not understand.	I can do it with help.	I can do it on my own.	I can teach someone else.

	Rating	Date
B.1 Probability		
Learning Target: Understand how the probability of an event indicates its likelihood.	1 2 3 4	
I can identify possible outcomes of an experiment.	1 2 3 4	
I can use probability and relative frequency to describe the likelihood of an event.	1 2 3 4	
I can use relative frequency to make predictions.	1 2 3 4	

B.1 Practice

You randomly choose one shape from the bag.
(a) Find the number of ways the event can occur.
(b) Find the favorable outcomes of the event.

1. Choosing a triangle

2. Choosing a star

3. Choosing *not* a square

4. Choosing *not* a circle

5. There are 12 cats and 6 dogs at the Humane Society. You randomly choose a pet.

   a. How many possible outcomes are there?

   b. In how many ways can you choose a cat?

   c. In how many ways can you choose a dog?

   d. Describe the likelihood that you choose a dog. Explain your reasoning.

Describe the likelihood of the event from the given information.

6. The school bus arrives late $\frac{2}{7}$ of the time. The school bus arrives on time.

7. The probability that it rains during a hurricane is 1. It rains during a hurricane.

8. There is an 85% chance that you will go to the concert. You do not go to the concert.

9. A store has 30 blue pens, 18 black pens, and 12 red pens in stock. You buy 30 blue pens and 5 red pens. Describe the likelihood of each event before and after your purchase.

   a. Randomly choosing a blue pen at the store.

   b. Randomly choosing a black pen at the store.

   c. Randomly choosing a red pen at the store.

B.2 Experimental and Theoretical Probability
For use with Exploration B.2

Learning Target: Develop probability models using experimental and theoretical probability.

Success Criteria:
- I can explain the meanings of experimental probability and theoretical probability.
- I can find experimental and theoretical probabilities.
- I can use probability to make predictions.

---

1   EXPLORATION: Conducting Experiments

Work with a partner. Conduct the following experiments and find the relative frequencies.

Experiment 1

- Flip a quarter 25 times and record whether each flip lands heads up or tails up.

Experiment 2

- Toss a thumbtack onto a table 25 times and record whether each toss lands point up or on its side.

Big Ideas Math: Modeling Real Life Grade 7 Advanced
Student Journal

B.2 Experimental and Theoretical Probability (continued)

a. Combine your results with those of your classmates. Do the relative frequencies change? What do you notice?

b. Everyone in your school conducts each experiment and you combine the results. How do you expect the relative frequencies to change? Explain.

c. How many times in 1000 flips do you expect a quarter to land heads up? How many times in 1000 tosses to you expect a thumbtack to land point up? Explain your reasoning.

d. In a *uniform probability model*, each outcome is equally likely to occur. Can you use a uniform probability model to describe either experiment? Explain.

Name _____ **Date** _____

B.2 Notetaking with Vocabulary

Vocabulary:

Notes:

B.2 Self-Assessment

Use the scale below to rate your understanding of the learning target and the success criteria.

1	2	3	4
I do not understand.	I can do it with help.	I can do it on my own.	I can teach someone else.

	Rating	Date
B.2 Experimental and Theoretical Probability		
Learning Target: Develop probability models using experimental and theoretical probability.	1 2 3 4	
I can explain the meanings of experimental probability and theoretical probability.	1 2 3 4	
I can find experimental and theoretical probabilities.	1 2 3 4	
I can use probability to make predictions.	1 2 3 4	

B.2 Practice

You have four sticks. Two sticks have one blue side and one pink side. One stick has 2 blue sides. One stick has 2 pink sides. You throw the sticks 20 times and record the results. Use the table to find the experimental probability of the event.

Outcome	Frequency
3 blue, 1 pink	7
2 blue, 2 pink	9
1 blue, 3 pink	4

1. tossing 1 pink and 3 blue

2. tossing the same number of blue and pink

3. *not* tossing 3 pink

4. tossing at most 2 blue

5. You check 30 containers of yogurt. Seven of them have an expiration date within the next 3 days.

   a. What is the experimental probability that a container of yogurt will have an expiration date within the next 3 days?

   b. Out of 120 containers of yogurt, how many would you expect to have an expiration date within the next 3 days? Explain.

6. You flip 3 coins 50 times, and flipping 3 tails occurs 6 times, flipping 3 heads occurs 7 times.

   a. What is the theoretical probability that you flip 3 heads?

   b. What is the theoretical probability that you flip less than 3 heads?

   c. What is the experimental probability that you flip 3 heads?

   d. What is the experimental probability that you flip 3 tails?

   e. How many times would you expect to flip 3 tails out of 200 trials of flipping 3 coins? Explain.

7. Each letter of the alphabet is printed on an index card. After removing the cards that spell the word "vowel," what is the theoretical probability of randomly choosing a vowel? Explain.

8. There are 12 cats and 8 dogs in the pet store.

   a. What is the theoretical probability that a randomly chosen pet is a cat?

   b. Two days later, there are half as many cats in the pet store. The theoretical probability that a randomly chosen pet is a cat is half that of two days earlier. How many dogs are in the pet store two days later?

B.3 Compound Events
For use with Exploration B.3

Learning Target: Find sample spaces and probabilities of compound events.

Success Criteria:
- I can find the sample space of two or more events.
- I can find the total number of possible outcomes of two or more events.
- I can find probabilities of compound events.

---

1 EXPLORATION: Comparing Combination Locks

Work with a partner. You are buying a combination lock. You have three choices.

a. One lock has 3 wheels. Each wheel is numbered from 0 to 9. How many possible outcomes are there for each wheel? How many possible combinations are there?

b. How can you use the number of possible outcomes on each wheel to determine the number of possible combinations?

Big Ideas Math: Modeling Real Life Grade 7 Advanced

B.3 **Compound Events** (continued)

   c. Another lock has one wheel numbered from 0 to 39. Each combination uses a sequence of three numbers. How many possible combinations are there?

   d. Another lock has 4 wheels as described. How many possible combinations are there?

     Wheel 1: 0–9

     Wheel 2: A–J

     Wheel 3: K–T

     Wheel 4: 0–9

   e. For which lock are you least likely to guess the combination? Why?

Notetaking with Vocabulary

Vocabulary:

Notes:

B.3 Self-Assessment

Use the scale below to rate your understanding of the learning target and the success criteria.

1	**2**	**3**	**4**
I do not understand.	I can do it with help.	I can do it on my own.	I can teach someone else.

	Rating	Date
B.3 Compound Events		
Learning Target: Find sample spaces and probabilities of compound events.	1 2 3 4	
I can find the sample space of two or more events.	1 2 3 4	
I can find the total number of possible outcomes of two or more events.	1 2 3 4	
I can find probabilities of compound events.	1 2 3 4	

B.3 Practice

Use a tree diagram to find the sample space and the total number of possible outcomes.

1.

Game	
Coin	Quarter, Dime, Nickel, Penny
Card	King, Queen, Jack

Use the Fundamental Counting Principle to find the total number of possible outcomes.

2.

Sandwich	
Bread	Italian, Wheat
Meat	Ham, Roast Beef, Salami
Cheese	American, Provolone, Swiss

3. Your computer password contains six characters. Each character is either a number or a letter. How many different passwords are possible? If numbers and letters cannot be used more than once, how many passwords are possible?

4. To win the jackpot you must match five numbers from 1 to 40. What is the probability that you will win the jackpot?

5. You need to hang seven pictures in a straight line.

   a. In how many ways can this be accomplished?

   b. If the picture of your great-grandfather must be in the middle, how many ways can the seven pictures be hung? Explain.

6. A license plate must contain two letters followed by four digits. How many license plates are possible? If the rule changed to five digits instead of four digits, how many more license plates would be possible?

B.4 Simulations
For use with Exploration B.4

Learning Target: Design and use simulations to find probabilities of compound events.

Success Criteria:
- I can design a simulation to model a real-life situation.
- I can recognize favorable outcomes in a simulation.
- I can use simulations to find experimental probabilities.

---

1 EXPLORATION: Using a Simulation

Work with a partner. A basketball player makes 80% of her free throw attempts.

a. Is she likely to make at least two of her next three free throws? Explain your reasoning.

b. The table shows 30 randomly generated numbers from 0 to 999. Let each number represent three shots. How can you use the digits of these numbers to represent made shots and missed shots?

838	617	282	341	785
747	332	279	082	716
937	308	800	994	689
198	025	853	591	813
672	289	518	649	540
865	631	227	004	840

B.4 **Simulations** (continued)

c. Use the table to estimate the probability that of her next three free throws,
she makes

- exactly two free throws.

- at most one free throw.

- at least two free throws.

- at least two free throws in a row.

d. The experiment used in parts (b) and (c) is called a *simulation*. Another
player makes $\frac{3}{5}$ of her free throws. Describe a simulation that can be used to
estimate the probability that she makes three of her next four free throws.

Notetaking with Vocabulary

Vocabulary:

Notes:

B.4 Self-Assessment

Use the scale below to rate your understanding of the learning target and
the success criteria.

1	2	3	4
I do not understand.	I can do it with help.	I can do it on my own.	I can teach someone else.

	Rating	Date
B.4 Simulations		
Learning Target: Design and use simulations to find probabilities of compound events.	1 2 3 4	
I can design a simulation to model a real-life situation.	1 2 3 4	
I can recognize favorable outcomes in a simulation.	1 2 3 4	
I can use simulations to find experimental probabilities.	1 2 3 4	

B.4 Practice

A medicine is effective on 70% of patients. The table shows 30 randomly generated numbers from 0 to 999. Use the table to estimate the probability of the event.

028	837	618	205	984
724	301	249	946	925
042	113	696	985	632
312	085	997	198	398
117	240	853	373	597
606	077	016	012	695

1. The medicine is effective on at least two of the next three patients.

2. The medicine is effective on none of the next three patients.

Design and use a simulation to find the experimental probability.

3. A bowler hits the head pin 90% of the time that all ten pins are standing. What is the experimental probability that the bowler hits the head pin exactly four of the next five times that all ten pins are standing?

4. In your garden, 40% of your pineapple plants produce a pineapple each year. What is the experimental probability that at most two of the three pineapple plants produce a pineapple this year? Explain.

5. A fitness center randomly selects one of five free gifts to send to each new customer. Gifts include a workout towel, a water bottle, a heart monitor, a T-shirt, and a gift card to the marketplace. What is the experimental probability that for the next two customers, one receives a heart monitor and one receives a gift card to the marketplace? Explain.

Design and use a simulation with number cubes to estimate the probability.

6. Your younger sibling will finish his or her dinner plate two out of every six dinners. Estimate the probability that at least two of the next three dinner plates are finished. Explain.

7. You win your favorite video game $\frac{5}{6}$ of the time. Estimate the probability that you will win your favorite video game exactly three of the next four times you play the game. Explain.

Name_____ Date_____

 Chapter B **Chapter Self-Assessment**

Use the scale below to rate your understanding of the learning target and the success criteria.

1	**2**	**3**	**4**
I do not understand.	I can do it with help.	I can do it on my own.	I can teach someone else.

	Rating	Date
B.1 Probability		
Learning Target: Understand how the probability of an event indicates its likelihood.	1　2　3　4	
I can identify possible outcomes of an experiment.	1　2　3　4	
I can use probability and relative frequency to describe the likelihood of an event.	1　2　3　4	
I can use relative frequency to make predictions.	1　2　3　4	
B.2 Experimental and Theoretical Probability		
Learning Target: Develop probability models using experimental and theoretical probability.	1　2　3　4	
I can explain the meanings of experimental probability and theoretical probability.	1　2　3　4	
I can find experimental and theoretical probabilities.	1　2　3　4	
I can use probability to make predictions.	1　2　3　4	
B.3 Compound Events		
Learning Target: Find sample spaces and probabilities of compound events.	1　2　3　4	
I can find the sample space of two or more events.	1　2　3　4	
I can find the total number of possible outcomes of two or more events.	1　2　3　4	
I can find probabilities of compound events.	1　2　3　4	

Chapter B Chapter Self-Assessment (continued)

	Rating	Date
B.4 Simulations		
Learning Target: Design and use simulations to find probabilities of compound events.	1 2 3 4	
I can design a simulation to model a real-life situation.	1 2 3 4	
I can recognize favorable outcomes in a simulation.	1 2 3 4	
I can use simulations to find experimental probabilities.	1 2 3 4	

Name_____ Date_____

Find the mean of the data.

1. 15, 21, 10, 18, 26, 23, 18, 20, 21, 19, 25, 22

2. 76, 105, 98, 198, 103, 84, 112, 88, 101, 81, 92

3. 47.5, 47.3, 47.2, 47.4, 47.9, 47.5, 47.1, 47.6, 47.7

4. Identify any outliers in Exercises 1–3. Describe the effect of the outlier on the mean.

Chapter C Review & Refresh (continued)

Find the median, first quartile, third quartile, and interquartile range of the data.

5. 45, 68, 59, 38, 21, 26, 58, 46, 33, 41, 52, 51, 25

6. 187, 225, 174, 179, 231, 208, 110, 200, 194, 215, 199, 212

7. 2.6, 4.9, 1.4, 1.7, 2.3, 9.4, 3.8, 3.5, 7.6, 4.4, 5.0, 3.1, 2.6, 6.8, 9.1

8. Use the interquartile range to identify any outliers in Exercises 5–7.

Name_____ Date_____

Samples and Populations
For use with Exploration C.1

Learning Target: Understand how to use random samples to make conclusions about a population.

Success Criteria:
- I can explain why a sample is biased or unbiased.
- I can explain why conclusions made from a biased sample may not be valid.
- I can use an unbiased sample to make a conclusion about a population.

---

1 EXPLORATION: Using Samples of Populations

Work with a partner. You want to make conclusions about the favorite extracurricular activities of students at your school.

   a. Identify the population. Then identify five samples of the population.

   b. When a sample is selected *at random*, each member of the population is equally likely to be selected. Are any of the samples in part (a) selected at random? Explain your reasoning.

C.1   **Samples and Populations** (continued)

  c. How are the samples below different? Is each conclusion valid? Explain
     your reasoning.

> You ask 20 members of the school
> band about their favorite activity.
> The diagram shows the results. You
> conclude that band is the favorite
> activity of 70% of the students in
> your school.

Favorite Activity

> You ask every eighth student who enters the
> school about their favorite activity. One student
> says glee club for every nine that name a
> different activity. You conclude that glee club is
> the favorite activity of 10% of the students in
> your school.

  d. Write a survey question about a topic that interests you. How can you
     choose people to survey so that you can use the results to make a valid
     conclusion?

Notetaking with Vocabulary

Vocabulary:

Notes:

C.1 **Self-Assessment**

Use the scale below to rate your understanding of the learning target and the success criteria.

1	2	3	4
I do not understand.	I can do it with help.	I can do it on my own.	I can teach someone else.

	Rating	Date
C.1 Samples and Populations		
Learning Target: Understand how to use random samples to make conclusions about a population.	1 2 3 4	
I can explain why a sample is biased or unbiased.	1 2 3 4	
I can explain why conclusions made from a biased sample may not be valid.	1 2 3 4	
I can use an unbiased sample to make a conclusion about a population.	1 2 3 4	

C.1 Practice

1. You want to know the number of fans at the Miami Dolphins and Dallas Cowboys game that think the Dolphins will win. You survey 50 fans with season tickets for the Dolphins.

   a. What is the population of your survey?

   b. What is the sample of your survey?

   c. Is the sample biased or unbiased? Explain.

2. Which sample is better for making an estimate? Explain.

Estimate the number of families in your town with two or more children.	
Sample A	A random sample of 10 families living near your home
Sample B	A random sample of 10 families living in your town

Determine whether you would survey the population or a sample. Explain.

3. You want to know the favorite clothing store of the students at your school.

4. You want to know the favorite topic of students in your history class.

5. An administrator surveys a random sample of 48 out of 900 middle school students. Using the survey results, the administrator estimates that 225 students are in favor of the new dress code. How many of the 48 students surveyed were in favor of the new dress code?

6. The table show the results of a survey of 75 randomly chosen seventh graders from your school. There are 300 seventh graders in your school. In the survey, each individual was asked to name his or her favorite type of music.

Music	Frequency
Rock	20
Country	23
Rap	30
Classical	2

   a. Estimate the number of seventh graders in your school whose favorite type of music is country.

   b. If you were to repeat the survey using randomly chosen adults, would you predict that the results of the adult survey will be different if you surveyed adults in their 30s versus adults in their 70s? Explain your reasoning.

C.2 Using Random Samples to Describe Populations
For use with Exploration C.2

Learning Target: Understand variability in samples of a population.

Success Criteria: • I can use multiple random samples to make conclusions about a population.

   • I can use multiple random samples to examine variation in estimates.

---

1   EXPLORATION: Exploring Variability in Samples

Work with a partner. Sixty percent of all seventh graders have visited a planetarium.

   a. Design a simulation using packing peanuts. Mark 60% of the packing peanuts and put them in a paper bag. What does choosing a marked peanut represent?

   b. Simulate a sample of 25 students by choosing peanuts from the bag, replacing the peanut each time. Record the results.

C.2 **Using Random Samples to Describe Populations** (continued)

c. Find the percent of students in the sample who have visited a planetarium. Compare this value to the actual percent of all seventh graders who have visited a planetarium.

d. Record the percent in part (c) from each pair in the class. Use a dot plot to display the data. Describe the variation in the data.

Name_____ Date_____

C.2 Notetaking with Vocabulary

Vocabulary:

Notes:

C.2 Self-Assessment

Use the scale below to rate your understanding of the learning target and the success criteria.

1	2	3	4
I do not understand.	I can do it with help.	I can do it on my own.	I can teach someone else.

	Rating	Date
C.2 Using Random Samples to Describe Populations		
Learning Target: Understand variability in samples of a population.	1 2 3 4	
I can use multiple random samples to make conclusions about a population.	1 2 3 4	
I can use multiple random samples to examine variation in estimates.	1 2 3 4	

C.2 Practice

1. Work with a partner. Mark 30 small pieces of paper with an A, a B, or a C. Put the pieces of paper in a bag. Trade bags with other students in the class.

   a. Generate a sample by choosing a piece of paper from your bag 10 times, replacing the piece of paper each time. Record the number of times you choose each letter. Repeat this process to generate five more samples.

   b. Use each sample to make an estimate for the number of As and Bs in the bag. Then describe the variation of the six estimates. Make estimates for the numbers of As, Bs, and Cs in the bag based on all the samples.

   c. Take the pieces of paper out of the bag. How do your estimates compare to the population? Do you think you can make a more accurate estimate? If so, explain how.

2. Work with a partner. You want to know the mean number of hours students in band or orchestra practice their instruments each week. Prior research indicates that the maximum number of hours of practice is 14 hours per week.

   a. Use technology to simulate the hours of practice for 10 students in band or orchestra. Randomly generate 10 numbers from 0 to 14. Write down the results. Repeat the simulation 9 more times, writing down the results each time.

   b. Use each sample to make an estimate for the mean number of hours students in band or orchestra practice their instruments each week. Describe the variation of the estimates.

   c. Use all ten samples to make one estimate for the mean number of hours students in band or orchestra practice their instruments each week. How does your estimate compare to the mean of the entire data set?

   d. Use each sample to make an estimate for the median number of hours students in band or orchestra practice their instruments each week. Describe the variation of the estimates.

   e. Use all ten samples to make one estimate for the median number of hours students in band or orchestra practice their instruments each week.

C.3 Comparing Populations
For use with Exploration C.3

Learning Target: Compare populations using measures of center and variation.

Success Criteria:
- I can find the measures of center and variation of a data set.
- I can describe the visual overlap of two data distributions numerically.
- I can determine whether there is a significant difference in the measures of center of two data sets.

---

1 **EXPLORATION:** Comparing Two Data Distributions

Work with a partner.

a. Does each data display show *overlap*? Explain.

Big Ideas Math: Modeling Real Life Grade 7 Advanced
Student Journal

C.3 **Comparing Populations** (continued)

Ages of People in Two Exercise Classes

10:00 A.M. Class								8:00 P.M. Class					
							1	8	9				
							2	1	2	2	7	9	9
							3	0	3	4	5	7	
9	7	3	2	2	2		4	0					
	7	5	4	3	1		5						
			7	0	0		6						
					0		7						

Key: 2 | 4 | 0 = 42 and 40 years

b. How can you describe the overlap of two data distributions using words? How can you describe the overlap numerically?

c. In which pair of data sets is the difference in the measures of center the most significant? Explain your reasoning.

Name_____ Date_____

 Notetaking with Vocabulary

Vocabulary:

Notes:

 Self-Assessment

Use the scale below to rate your understanding of the learning target and
the success criteria.

1	2	3	4
I do not understand.	I can do it with help.	I can do it on my own.	I can teach someone else.

	Rating	Date
C.3 Comparing Populations		
Learning Target: Compare populations using measures of center and variation.	1 2 3 4	
I can find the measures of center and variation of a data set.	1 2 3 4	
I can describe the visual overlap of two data distributions numerically.	1 2 3 4	
I can determine whether there is a significant difference in the measures of center of two data sets.	1 2 3 4	

C.3 Practice

1. A scientist experiments with a new type of corn. The dot plots show the heights of corn stalks in two gardens. Experimental corn was planted in Garden A. Traditional corn was planted in Garden B.

Garden A

Garden B

a. Compare the data sets using measures of center and variation.

b. Express the difference in the measures of center as a multiple of the measure of variation.

c. If the experimental corn stalks are significantly taller than the traditional corn, the scientist will repeat the experiment in a field rather than a garden. Should the scientist repeat the experiment in a field? Justify your answer.

2. The double box-and-whisker plot represents the runs scored per game by two softball teams during a 15-game season.

a. Compare the data sets using measures of center and variation.

b. Which data set is more likely to contain a value of 3?

c. Is the number of runs scored per game significantly greater for one team than the other? Explain.

Name_____ Date_____

Learning Target: Use random samples to compare populations.

Success Criteria:
- I can compare random samples using measures of center and variation.
- I can recognize whether random samples are likely to be representative of a population.
- I can compare populations using multiple random samples.

---

1 EXPLORATION: Using Random Samples

Work with a partner. You want to compare the numbers of hours spent on homework each week by male and female students in your state. You take a random sample of 15 male students and 15 female students throughout the state.

Male Students				
1.5	3	0	2.5	1
8	2.5	1	3	0
6.5	1	5	0	5

Female Students				
4	0	3	1	1
5	1	3	5.5	10
2	0	6	3.5	2

a. Compare the data in each sample.

b. Are the samples likely to be representative of all male and female students in your state? Explain.

C.4   **Using Random Samples to Compare Populations** (continued)

c. You take 100 random samples of 15 male students in your state and
   100 random samples of 15 female students in your state and record the
   median of each sample. The double box-and-whisker plot shows the
   distributions of the sample medians. Compare the distributions in the
   double box-and-whisker plot with the distributions of the data in the tables.

d. What can you conclude from the double box-and-whisker plot? Explain.

e. How can you use random samples to make accurate comparisons of
   two populations?

Notetaking with Vocabulary

Vocabulary:

Notes:

 Self-Assessment

Use the scale below to rate your understanding of the learning target and the success criteria.

1	**2**	**3**	**4**
I do not understand.	I can do it with help.	I can do it on my own.	I can teach someone else.

	Rating	Date
C.4 Using Random Samples to Compare Populations		
Learning Target: Use random samples to compare populations	1 2 3 4	
I can compare random samples using measures of center and variation.	1 2 3 4	
I can recognize whether random samples are likely to be representative of a population.	1 2 3 4	
I can compare populations using multiple random samples.	1 2 3 4	

Name _____ Date _____

C.4 Practice

1. The tables show the numbers of attendees at random pep rallies for football and basketball games at a school during the last 5 years.

Football Pep Rally Attendance

174	175	200	169	178	171
165	187	159	170	184	196
205	231	198	310	152	178

Basketball Pep Rally Attendance

143	178	154	167	204	199
254	147	179	162	189	203
217	214	187	210	288	287

a. Find the mean, median, mode, range, interquartile range, and mean absolute deviation for the samples.

b. When comparing the two samples using measures of center and variation, would you use the mean and the MAD, or the median and the IQR? Explain.

c. Compare the samples.

d. Can you determine which pep rally is more popular?

2. Two manufacturing plants each produce 120 frozen food products. A scientist takes 10 samples of 12 frozen food products from each lab and records the number that pass an inspection. Are the samples likely to be representative of all the frozen food products for each manufacturing plant? If so, which lab has more frozen food products that will pass the inspection? Justify your answer.

Manufacturing Plant A

9	8	12	7	9
10	7	11	8	9

Manufacturing Plant B

12	11	11	10	12
12	10	11	12	12

Chapter Self-Assessment

Use the scale below to rate your understanding of the learning target and the success criteria.

1	2	3	4
I do not understand.	I can do it with help.	I can do it on my own.	I can teach someone else.

	Rating	Date
C.1 Samples and Populations		
Learning Target: Understand how to use random samples to make conclusions about a population.	1 2 3 4	
I can explain why a sample is biased or unbiased.	1 2 3 4	
I can explain why conclusions made from a biased sample may not be valid.	1 2 3 4	
I can use an unbiased sample to make a conclusion about a population.	1 2 3 4	
C.2 Using Random Samples to Describe Populations		
Learning Target: Understand variability in samples of a population.	1 2 3 4	
I can use multiple random samples to make conclusions about a population.	1 2 3 4	
I can use multiple random samples to examine variation in estimates.	1 2 3 4	
C.3 Comparing Populations		
Learning Target: Compare populations using measures of center and variation.	1 2 3 4	
I can find the measures of center and variation of a data set.	1 2 3 4	
I can describe the visual overlap of two data distributions numerically.	1 2 3 4	
I can determine whether there is a significant difference in the measures of center of two data sets.	1 2 3 4	

Chapter Self-Assessment (continued)

	Rating	Date
C.4 Using Random Samples to Compare Populations		
Learning Target: Use random samples to compare populations.	1 2 3 4	
I can compare random samples using measures of center and variation.	1 2 3 4	
I can recognize whether random samples are likely to be representative of a population.	1 2 3 4	
I can compare populations using multiple random samples.	1 2 3 4	

Name_____ / _____ Date_____

Identify the basic shapes in the figure.

1.

2.

3.

4.

5. Identify the basic shapes that make up the top of the teacher's desk.

Chapter D **Review & Refresh** (continued)

Use a protractor to find the measure of the angle. Then classify the angle as *acute*, *obtuse*, *right*, or *straight*.

6.

7.

8.

9.

Use a protractor to draw an angle with the given measure.

10. 80°

11. 175°

D.1 Circles and Circumference
For use with Exploration D.1

Learning Target: Find the circumference of a circle.

Success Criteria:
- I can explain the relationship between the diameter and circumference of a circle.
- I can use a formula to find the circumference of a circle.

---

1 EXPLORATION: Using a Compass to Draw a Circle

Work with a partner. Set a compass to 2 inches and draw a circle.

a. Draw a line from one side of the circle to the other that passes through the center. What is the length of the line? This is called the *diameter* of the circle.

b. Estimate the distance around the circle. This is called the *circumference* of the circle. Explain how you found your answer.

D.1 **Circles and Circumference** (continued)

2 **EXPLORATION:** Exploring Diameter and Circumference

Work with a partner.

a. Roll a cylindrical object on a flat surface to find the circumference of the circular base.

b. Measure the diameter of the circular base. Which is greater, the diameter or the circumference? how many times greater?

c. Compare your answers in part (b) with the rest of the class. What do you notice?

d. Without measuring, how can you find the circumference of a circle with a given diameter? Use your method to estimate the circumference of the circle in Exploration 1.

D.1 Notetaking with Vocabulary

Vocabulary:

Notes:

D.1 Self-Assessment

Use the scale below to rate your understanding of the learning target and the success criteria.

1	**2**	**3**	**4**
I do not understand.	I can do it with help.	I can do it on my own.	I can teach someone else.

	Rating	Date
D.1 Circles and Circumference		
Learning Target: Find the circumference of a circle.	1 2 3 4	
I can explain the relationship between the diameter and circumference of a circle.	1 2 3 4	
I can use a formula to find the circumference of a circle.	1 2 3 4	

D.1 Practice

Find the circumference of the circle. Use 3.14 or $\frac{22}{7}$ for π.

1.

26 m

2.

6 ft

3.

42 in.

Find the perimeter of the semicircular region.

4.

28 yd

5.

7.5 ft

6.

11 cm

7. Consider the circles *A*, *B*, *C*, and *D*.

A

2.5 ft

B

24 in.

C

32 ft

D

84 in.

a. Without calculating, which circle has the greatest circumference? Explain.

b. Without calculating, which circle has the least circumference? Explain.

c. Find the circumference of each circle in feet. How many times larger is the greatest circumference than the least circumference? How could you find this answer without calculating?

8. A coaster has a circumference of 12.56 inches. Suppose the same amount of coaster is visible around the bottom of a glass as shown. What is the circumference of the glass?

0.5 in.   0.5 in.

9. Are the side lengths of the squares in Diagram A and Diagram B equivalent? Explain your reasoning.

Diagram A   Diagram B

10 ft

1 ft

10. You release a ball with a radius of 1 inch into a pipe as shown. How many times will the ball rotate before it falls out of the other end of the pipe?

1 in.

5 ft

Not drawn to scale

D.2 Areas of Circles
For use with Exploration D.2

Learning Target: Find the area of a circle.

Success Criteria:
- I can estimate the area of a circle.
- I can use a formula to find the area of a circle.

---

1 **EXPLORATION:** Estimating the Area of a Circle

Work with a partner. Each grid contains a circle with a diameter of 4 centimeters. Use each grid to estimate the area of the circle. Which estimate should be closest to the actual area? Explain.

  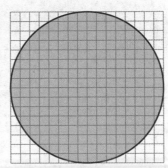

D.2 Areas of Circles (continued)

2 EXPLORATION: Writing a Formula for the Area of a Circle

Work with a partner. A student draws a circle with radius *r* and divides the circle into 24 equal sections (*). The student cuts out each section and arranges the sections to form a shape that resembles a parallelogram.

a. Use the diagram to write a formula for the area *A* of a circle in terms of the radius *r*. Explain your reasoning.

b. Use the formula to check your estimates in Exploration 1.

* Circle is available in the back of the Student Journal.

Notetaking with Vocabulary

Vocabulary:

Notes:

D.2 Self-Assessment

Use the scale below to rate your understanding of the learning target and the success criteria.

1	**2**	**3**	**4**
I do not understand.	I can do it with help.	I can do it on my own.	I can teach someone else.

	Rating	Date
D.2 Areas of Circles		
Learning Target: Find the area of a circle.	1 2 3 4	
I can estimate the area of a circle.	1 2 3 4	
I can use a formula to find the area of a circle.	1 2 3 4	

D.2 Practice

Find the area of the circle. Use 3.14 or $\frac{22}{7}$ for π.

1.

35 in.

2.

2.5 m

3.

48 mm

Find the area of the semicircle.

4.

20 in.

5.

16 m

6.

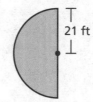

21 ft

7. The shadow of an object is roughly the same size as the object. What is the area of the circular shadow of the hot air balloon?

56 ft

8. How many *square feet* of the ground are sprayed by the beach shower?

72 in.

9. The radius of the small circle is half the radius of the large circle.

   a. Use the radius r to write a formula for the area of the large circle.

   b. Use the radius $\frac{r}{2}$ to write a formula for the area of the small circle.

   c. How does the area of a circle compare to the area of another circle whose radius is twice as large? Explain your reasoning.

r

10. The number of square inches of a circle's area is equal to the number of inches of its circumference. What is the radius of the circle? Explain how you found your answer.

D.3 Perimeters and Areas of Composite Figures
For use with Exploration D.3

Learning Target: Find perimeters and areas of composite figures.

Success Criteria:
- I can use a grid to estimate perimeters and areas.
- I can identify the shapes that make up a composite figure.
- I can find the perimeters and areas of shapes that make up composite figures.

---

1 EXPLORATION: Submitting a Bid

Work with a partner. You want to bid on a project for the pool shown. The project involves ordering and installing the brown tile that borders the pool, and ordering a custom-made tarp to cover the surface of the pool. In the figure, each grid square represents 1 square foot.

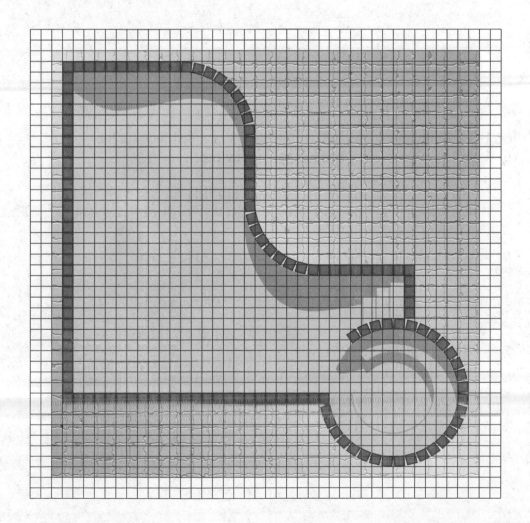

D.3 **Perimeters and Areas of Composite Figures** (continued)

- **You pay $5 per linear foot for the tile.**

- **You pay $4 per square foot for the tarp.**

- **It takes you about 15 minutes to install each foot of tile.**

a. Estimate the total cost for the tile and the tarp.

b. Write a bid for how much you will charge for the project. Include the hourly wage you will receive. Estimate your total profit.

Name_____ Date_____

D.3 **Notetaking with Vocabulary**

Vocabulary:

Notes:

D.3 **Self-Assessment**

Use the scale below to rate your understanding of the learning target and the success criteria.

1	2	3	4
I do not understand.	I can do it with help.	I can do it on my own.	I can teach someone else.

	Rating	Date
D.3 Perimeters and Areas of Composite Figures		
Learning Target: Find perimeters and areas of composite figures.	1 2 3 4	
I can use a grid to estimate perimeters and areas.	1 2 3 4	
I can identify the shapes that make up a composite figure.	1 2 3 4	
I can find the perimeters and areas of shapes that make up composite figures.	1 2 3 4	

D.3 Practice

Estimate the perimeter and the area of the shaded figure.

1.

2.

3.
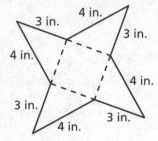

Find the perimeter and the area of the figure.

4.
5 m
3.5 m   3.5 m
1.5 m
3.5 m   3.5 m
5 m

5.
17 cm
34 cm

6.

3 in.   4 in.
4 in.   3 in.
4 in.
3 in.
4 in.   3 in.

7. Describe and correct the error in finding the perimeter of the figure.

2 ft
7 ft

✗   Perimeter ≈ 2 + 7 + 2 + 21.98
         = 32.98 ft

8. A shrub has been cut and trimmed
into the shape of an "F". The owner
has hired a landscaper to decrease
the perimeter of the shrub by 10 feet.
Draw a diagram of how the landscaper
might do this. Is there more than one
way? Explain.

12 ft
3 ft
3 ft
20 ft   5 ft
11 ft
3 ft

9. A school has a garden in the shape
of a pencil. A fence is to be built around
the garden. The fence costs $2.75 per foot.
How much will it cost to install the fence?

20 ft
9 ft
12 ft
9 ft

D.4 Constructing Polygons
For use with Exploration D.4

Learning Target: Construct a polygon with given measures.

Success Criteria:
- I can use technology to draw polygons.
- I can determine whether given measures result in one triangle, many triangles, or no triangle.
- I can draw polygons given angle measures or side lengths.

---

1 EXPLORATION: Using Technology to Draw Polygons

Work with a partner.

a. Use geometry software to draw each polygon with the given side lengths or angle measures, if possible. Complete the table.

Side Lengths or Angle Measures	How many figures are possible?
i. 4 cm, 6 cm, 7 cm	
ii. 2 cm, 6 cm, 7 cm	
iii. 2 cm, 4 cm, 7 cm	
iv. 2 cm, 4 cm, 6 cm	
v. 2 in., 3 in., 3 in., 6 in.	
vi. 1 in., 1 in., 3 in., 6 in.	
vii. 1 in., 1 in., 3 in., 4 in.	
viii. 90°, 60°, 30°	
ix. 100°, 40°, 20°	
x. 50°, 60°, 70°	
xi. 20°, 80°, 100°	
xii. 20°, 50°, 50°, 60°	
xiii. 30°, 80°, 120°, 130°	
xiv. 60°, 60°, 120°, 120°	

D.4 **Constructing Polygons** (continued)

b. Without constructing, how can you tell whether it is possible to draw a triangle given three angle measures? three side lengths? Explain your reasoning.

c. Without constructing, how can you tell whether it is possible to draw a quadrilateral given four angle measures? four side lengths? Explain your reasoning.

Notetaking with Vocabulary

Vocabulary:

Notes:

Self-Assessment

Use the scale below to rate your understanding of the learning target and the success criteria.

1	**2**	**3**	**4**
I do not understand.	I can do it with help.	I can do it on my own.	I can teach someone else.

	Rating	Date
D.4 Constructing Polygons		
Learning Target: Construct a polygon with given measures.	1 2 3 4	
I can use technology to draw polygons.	1 2 3 4	
I can determine whether given measures result in one triangle, many triangles, or no triangle.	1 2 3 4	
I can draw polygons given angle measures or side lengths.	1 2 3 4	

D.4 Practice

Draw a triangle with the given angle measures, if possible.

1. 25°, 65°, 90°

2. 45°, 60°, 75°

3. Draw a triangle with the given description: a 110° angle connects to a 25° angle by a side of length 6 inches.

Determine whether you can construct *one*, *many*, or *no* triangle(s) with the given description. Explain your reasoning.

4. a triangle with a side length of 2 inches, a side length of 4 inches, and a side length of 5 inches

5. a scalene triangle with two side lengths of 7 centimeters

6. a triangle with one angle measure of 100° and one side length of 6 inches

7. Determine whether the statement is *true* or *false*. Explain your reasoning. You may use diagrams to explain your reasoning.

a. A rectangle with side lengths of 30 inches and 10 inches can be divided into two congruent squares.

b. A rectangle with side lengths of 30 inches and 10 inches can be divided into three congruent squares.

c. A parallelogram with opposite congruent side lengths of 6 feet and 3 feet can be divided into two congruent rhombuses.

d. A rectangle with side lengths of 30 inches and 10 inches can be divided into two congruent trapezoids.

e. A rhombus that has side lengths of 8 meters can be divided into two congruent parallelograms.

Construct a quadrilateral with the given description.

8. a kite with side lengths of 2 feet and 5 feet

9. a trapezoid with a base of length 4 meters and an opposite parallel side of length 1 meter

10. a rhombus with adjacent angles of 70° and 110°

D.5 Finding Unknown Angle Measures
For use with Exploration D.5

Learning Target: Use facts about angle relationships to find unknown angle measures.

Success Criteria:
- I can identify adjacent, complementary, supplementary, and vertical angles.
- I can use equations to find unknown angle measures.
- I can find unknown angle measures in real-life situations.

---

1 EXPLORATION: Using Rules About Angles

Work with a partner. The diagram shows pairs of *adjacent* angles and *vertical* angles. Vertical angles cannot be adjacent.

a. Which pair(s) of angles are adjacent angles? Explain.

b. Which pair(s) of angles are vertical angles? Explain.

c. Without using a protractor, find the values of x, y, and z. Explain your reasoning.

D.5 **Finding Unknown Angle Measures** (continued)

   d. Make a conjecture about the measures of any two vertical angles.

   e. Test your conjecture in part (d) using the diagram below. Explain why your
   conjecture is or is *not* true.

Name_____ Date_____

Vocabulary:

Notes:

D.5 Self-Assessment

Use the scale below to rate your understanding of the learning target and the success criteria.

1	**2**	**3**	**4**
I do not understand.	I can do it with help.	I can do it on my own.	I can teach someone else.

	Rating	Date
D.5 Finding Unknown Angle Measures		
Learning Target: Use facts about angle relationships to find unknown angle measures.	1　2　3　4	
I can identify adjacent, complementary, supplementary, and vertical angles.	1　2　3　4	
I can use equations to find unknown angle measures.	1　2　3　4	
I can find unknown angle measures in real-life situations.	1　2　3　4	

D.5 Practice

Name two pairs of adjacent angles and two pairs of vertical angles in the figure.

1.

2.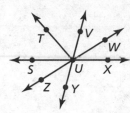

Classify the pair of angles. Then find the value of x.

3.

4.

5.

6.

7. Draw a figure in which ∠2 and ∠3 are acute vertical angles, ∠1 and ∠2 are supplementary angles, ∠2 and ∠5 are complementary angles, and ∠4 and ∠5 are adjacent angles.

8. Find the values of x and y.

9. The measures of two adjacent angles have a ratio of 3 : 5. The sum of the measures of the two adjacent angles is 120°. What is the measure of the larger angle?

10. Let x be an angle measure. Let c be the measure of the complement of the angle and let s be the measure of the supplement of the angle.

    a. Write an equation involving c and x.

    b. Write an equation involving s and x.

Name_____ Date _____

Chapter Self-Assessment

Use the scale below to rate your understanding of the learning target and the success criteria.

1	*2*	*3*	*4*
I do not understand.	I can do it with help.	I can do it on my own.	I can teach someone else.

	Rating	Date
D.1 Circles and Circumference		
Learning Target: Find the circumference of a circle.	1 2 3 4	
I can explain the relationship between the diameter and circumference of a circle.	1 2 3 4	
I can use a formula to find the circumference of a circle.	1 2 3 4	
D.2 Areas of Circles		
Learning Target: Find the area of a circle.	1 2 3 4	
I can estimate the area of a circle.	1 2 3 4	
I can use a formula to find the area of a circle.	1 2 3 4	
D.3 Perimeters and Areas of Composite Figures		
Learning Target: Find perimeters and areas of composite figures.	1 2 3 4	
I can use a grid to estimate perimeters and areas.	1 2 3 4	
I can identify the shapes that make up a composite figure.	1 2 3 4	
I can find the perimeters and areas of shapes that make up composite figures.	1 2 3 4	

Chapter Self-Assessment (continued)

	Rating	Date
D.4 Constructing Polygons		
Learning Target: Construct a polygon with given measures.	1 2 3 4	
I can use technology to draw polygons.	1 2 3 4	
I can determine whether given measures result in one triangle, many triangles, or no triangle.	1 2 3 4	
I can draw polygons given angle measures or side lengths.	1 2 3 4	
D.5 Finding Unknown Angle Measures		
Learning Target: Use facts about angle relationships to find unknown angle measures.	1 2 3 4	
I can identify adjacent, complementary, supplementary, and vertical angles.	1 2 3 4	
I can use equations to find unknown angle measures.	1 2 3 4	
I can find unknown angle measures in real-life situations.	1 2 3 4	

Chapter E Review & Refresh

Find the area of the square or rectangle.

1.

8 cm

8 cm

2.

7 yd

12 yd

3.

9.2 in.

6.4 in.

4.

$\frac{5}{6}$ m

$\frac{5}{6}$ m

5.

$1\frac{1}{3}$ mm

$2\frac{1}{3}$ mm

6.

21.3 ft

15.1 ft

7. An artist buys a square canvas with a side length of 2.5 feet. What is the area of the canvas?

Name _____ Date _____

Find the area of the triangle.

8.
4 cm
10 cm

9.
8 ft
3 ft

10.
7 m
6 m

11.
12 yd
5 yd

12.
5 in.
4 in.

13.
9 mm
2 mm

14. A spirit banner for a pep rally has the shape of a triangle. The base of the banner is 8 feet and the height is 6 feet. Find the area of the banner.

E.1 Surface Areas of Prisms
For use with Exploration E.1

Learning Target: Find the surface area of a prism.

Success Criteria:
- I can use a formula to find the surface area of a prism.
- I can find the lateral surface area of a prism.

---

1 EXPLORATION: Writing a Formula for Surface Area

Work with a partner.

a. Use the diagrams to write a formula for the surface area of a rectangular prism. Explain your reasoning.

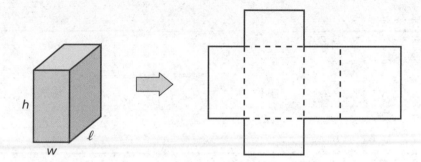

b. Choose dimensions for a rectangular prism. Then draw the prism and use your formula in part (a) to find the surface area.

E.1 **Surface Areas of Prisms** (continued)

2 **EXPLORATION:** Surface Area of Prisms

Work with a partner.

a. Identify the solid represented by the net (*). Then find the surface area of the solid.

b. Describe a method for finding the surface area of a prism.

* Net is available in the back of the Student Journal.

E.1 Notetaking with Vocabulary

Vocabulary:

Notes:

E.1 Self-Assessment

Use the scale below to rate your understanding of the learning target and the success criteria.

1	2	3	4
I do not understand.	I can do it with help.	I can do it on my own.	I can teach someone else.

	Rating	Date
E.1 Surface Areas of Prisms		
Learning Target: Find the surface area of a prism.	1 2 3 4	
I can use a formula to find the surface area of a prism.	1 2 3 4	
I can find the lateral surface area of a prism.	1 2 3 4	

Name _____ Date _____

Find the surface area of the prism.

1.

10 cm
30 cm
24 cm

2.

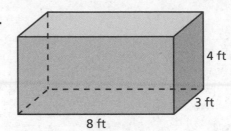

4 ft
3 ft
8 ft

3.

2 in.
12 in.
2 in.
2.8 in.

4.

14 m
28 m
14 m
10 m
20 m

5.

18 cm
10 cm
10 cm
4 cm
34 cm
6 cm

6.

6 ft
16 ft
6 ft

7. A graphing calculator is in the approximate shape of a rectangular prism.

9 cm
19 cm
2.5 cm

   a. Estimate the total surface area of the calculator.

   b. The window of the calculator is 6.5 centimeters long and 4.5 centimeters wide. Estimate the surface area of the graphing calculator without the window.

8. The least amount of wrapping paper needed to wrap a cube-shaped gift is 150 square inches. How long is one side of the gift?

E.2 Surface Areas of Cylinders
For use with Exploration E.2

Learning Target: Find the surface area of a cylinder.

Success Criteria:
- I can use a formula to find the surface area of a cylinder.
- I can find the lateral surface area of a cylinder.

---

1 EXPLORATION: Finding the Surface Area of a Cylinder

Work with a partner.

a. Make a net for a can. Name each shape in the net.

b. How are the dimensions of the paper related to the dimensions of the can?

E.2 **Surface Areas of Cylinders** (continued)

    c. Write a formula that represents the surface area of a cylinder with a height of h and bases with a radius of r.

    d. Estimate the dimensions of a can of tuna and a can of soup. Then use your formula in part (c) to estimate the surface area of each can.

Notetaking with Vocabulary

Vocabulary:

Notes:

E.2 **Self-Assessment**

Use the scale below to rate your understanding of the learning target and the success criteria.

1	**2**	**3**	**4**
I do not understand.	I can do it with help.	I can do it on my own.	I can teach someone else.

	Rating	Date
E.2 Surface Areas of Cylinders		
Learning Target: Find the surface area of a cylinder.	1 2 3 4	
I can use a formula to find the surface area of a cylinder.	1 2 3 4	
I can find the lateral surface area of a cylinder.	1 2 3 4	

E.2 Practice

Find the surface area of the cylinder. Round your answer to the nearest tenth if necessary.

1.

12 ft

5 ft

2.

1 cm

9 cm

Find the lateral surface area of the cylinder. Round your answer to the nearest tenth if necessary.

3.

13 m

10 m

4.

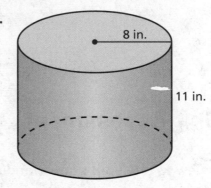

8 in.

11 in.

5. A quarter is worth $0.25 and a half dollar is worth $0.50.

  a. A quarter has a diameter of $\frac{15}{16}$ inch and a height of $\frac{1}{16}$ inch. Find the surface area of a quarter. Round your answer to the nearest hundredth.

  b. A half dollar has a diameter of $\frac{9}{8}$ inches and a height of $\frac{3}{32}$ inch. Find the surface area of a half dollar. Round your answer to the nearest hundredth.

  c. Show that the value of the coin is not proportional to the surface area of the coin.

  d. If the values of the coins were proportional to the surface areas of the coins, what would be the surface area of the half dollar? Round your answer to the nearest hundredth.

Name_____ Date_____

E.3 **Surface Areas of Pyramids**
For use with Exploration E.3

Learning Target: Find the surface area of a pyramid.

Success Criteria: • I can use a net to find the surface area of a regular pyramid.
• I can find the lateral surface area of a regular pyramid.

---

1 **EXPLORATION:** Making a Scale Model

Work with a partner. Each pyramid listed below has a square base.

Cheops Pyramid in Egypt

Side ≈ 230 m, Slant height ≈ 186 m

Louvre Pyramid in Paris

Side ≈ 35 m, Slant height ≈ 28 m

a. Draw a net for a scale model of one of the pyramids. Describe the scale factor.

E.3 **Surface Areas of Pyramids** (continued)

b. Find the lateral surface area of the real-life pyramid that you chose in part (a). Explain how you found your answer.

c. Draw a net for a pyramid with a non-rectangular base and find its lateral surface area. Explain how you found your answer.

Notetaking with Vocabulary

Vocabulary:

Notes:

E.3 **Self-Assessment**

Use the scale below to rate your understanding of the learning target and the success criteria.

1	2	3	4
I do not understand.	I can do it with help.	I can do it on my own.	I can teach someone else.

	Rating	Date
E.3 Surface Areas of Pyramids		
Learning Target: Find the surface area of a pyramid.	1 2 3 4	
I can use a net to find the surface area of a regular pyramid.	1 2 3 4	
I can find the lateral surface area of a regular pyramid.	1 2 3 4	

Name _____ Date _____

Find the surface area of the regular pyramid.

1.

4.3 cm

4.3 cm   6 cm

2.

21 ft

14 ft

14 ft   12.1 ft

3. Researchers have determined that a hip roof offers the most protection to a house during a hurricane.

   a. The house has a square base with a side length of 50 feet. The house has a variation of a hip roof in the shape of a regular pyramid with a square base. The roof extends 1 foot beyond the walls of the house on all sides. What is the length of each side of the base of the roof?

   b. The slant height of the roof is 35 feet. Find the sum of the areas of the lateral faces of the pyramid.

   c. A metal roof covering offers the most protection to a house during a hurricane. The cost of installing metal roof covering is $350 for every 100 square feet of roof. What is the cost of installing a metal roof covering on the house?

4. The surface area of a regular triangular pyramid is 197.1 square meters. The slant height is 12 meters. The area of the base is 35.1 square meters. What is the height of the triangular base?

5. The surface area of a regular pentagonal pyramid is 125 square yards. The base length is 5 yards. The area of the base is 37.5 square yards. What is the slant height of the pyramid?

Name_____ Date_____

E.4 **Volumes of Prisms**
For use with Exploration E.4

Learning Target: Find the volume of a prism.

Success Criteria:
- I can use a formula to find the volume of a prism.
- I can use the formula for the volume of a prism to find a missing dimension.

1 EXPLORATION: Finding a Formula for Volume

Work with a partner.

a. In the figures shown, each cube has a volume of 1 cubic unit. Compare the volume V (in cubic units) of each rectangular prism to the area B (in square units) of its base. What do you notice?

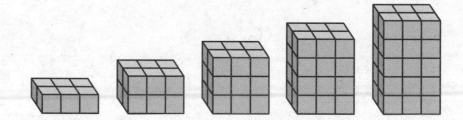

E.4 **Volumes of Prisms** (continued)

b. Repeat part (a) using the prisms below.

c. Use what you learned in parts (a) and (b) to write a formula that gives the volume of any prism.

Name_____ Date_____

Notetaking with Vocabulary

Vocabulary:

Notes:

E.4 Self-Assessment

Use the scale below to rate your understanding of the learning target and the success criteria.

1	2	3	4
I do not understand.	I can do it with help.	I can do it on my own.	I can teach someone else.

	Rating	Date
E.4 Volumes of Prisms		
Learning Target: Find the volume of a prism.	1 2 3 4	
I can use a formula to find the volume of a prism.	1 2 3 4	
I can use the formula for the volume of a prism to find a missing dimension.	1 2 3 4	

E.4 Practice

Find the volume of the prism.

1.

2.

3. A triangular prism has the measurements as shown.

   a. Find the volume of the prism.

   b. Find the volume of the triangular prism if the height of the triangular base is divided by 2.

   c. Explain the relationship between the volume in part (a) and the volume in part (b).

   d. Find the volume of the triangular prism if the height of the prism is divided by 2.

   e. Is the relationship between the volume in part (a) and the volume in part (d) the same as the relationship between the volume in part (a) and the volume in part (b)? Explain.

4. A water tank has the measurements shown. It is 30% full. How many gallons of water are needed to fill the water tank? (100 gal $= 0.37854$ m^3)

5. A mailbox is in the shape of a prism. The area of the base is 52 square inches and the height is 18 inches. What is the volume of the mailbox?

6. A chicken broth container is in the shape of a rectangular prism, with a length of 9.5 centimeters, a width of 6 centimeters, and a height of 16.5 centimeters. The container is 90% full. How many liters of chicken broth are in the container? (1 L $= 1000$ cm^3). Round your answer to the nearest hundredth.

7. How many cubic feet are in a cubic yard? Use a sketch to explain your reasoning.

E.5 Volumes of Pyramids
For use with Exploration E.5

Learning Target: Find the volume of a pyramid.

Success Criteria:
- I can use a formula to find the volume of a pyramid.
- I can use the volume of a pyramid to solve a real-life problem.

1 EXPLORATION: Finding a Formula for the Volume of a Pyramid

Work with a partner. Draw the two nets (*) on cardboard and cut them out. Fold and tape the nets to form an open cube and an open square pyramid. Both figures should have the same size square base and the same height.

a. Compare the volumes of the figures. What do you notice?

b. Use your observations in part (a) to write a formula for the volume of a pyramid.

* Nets are available in the back of the Student Journal.

E.5 **Volumes of Pyramids** (continued)

c. The rectangular prism below can be cut to form three pyramids. Use your
formula in part (b) to show that the sum of the volumes of the three
pyramids is equal to the volume of the prism.

E.5 Notetaking with Vocabulary

Vocabulary:

Notes:

E.5 Self-Assessment

Use the scale below to rate your understanding of the learning target and the success criteria.

1	2	3	4
I do not understand.	I can do it with help.	I can do it on my own.	I can teach someone else.

	Rating	Date
E.5 Volumes of Pyramids		
Learning Target: Find the volume of a pyramid.	1 2 3 4	
I can use a formula to find the volume of a pyramid.	1 2 3 4	
I can use the volume of a pyramid to solve a real-life problem.	1 2 3 4	

Name _____ Date _____

E.5 Practice

Find the volume of the pyramid.

1.

12 mm

15 mm

10 mm

2.

14 ft

5 ft

12 ft

3. An amusement park sells popcorn in pyramid-shaped containers. The park charges $0.50 for each 100 cubic centimeters of popcorn. If you purchase the large container, you receive a 25% discount. What is the price for each container? Explain your reasoning.

Pyramid A

22 cm

15 cm

25 cm

Pyramid B

15 in.

$B = 40$ in.²

4   A pyramid has a rectangular base with length of 15 feet and a width of 8 feet. The height of the pyramid is 10 feet.

   a. Find the volume of the pyramid.

   b. When the pyramid was being built, the original base was dropped and it split in two pieces. Each piece was a triangle with a base of 15 feet and a height of 8 feet. Pyramids were made with these two bases, each with a height of 10 feet. Find the combined volume of the two pyramids.

   c. Is the combined volume *greater than*, *less than*, or the *same as* the volume of the pyramid. Explain your reasoning.

5. A triangular pyramid has a volume of 350 cubic centimeters and a height of 10 centimeters. Find one possible set of dimensions of the base.

E.6 Cross Sections of Three-Dimensional Figures
For use with Exploration E.6

Learning Target: Describe the cross sections of a solid.

Success Criteria:
- I can explain the meaning of a cross section.
- I can describe cross sections of prisms and pyramids.
- I can describe cross sections of cylinders and cones.

---

1 EXPLORATION: Describing Cross Sections

Work with a partner. A baker is thinking of different ways to slice zucchini bread that is in the shape of a rectangular prism. The shape that is formed by the cut is called a *cross section*.

Cross section

a. What is the shape of the cross section when the baker slices the bread vertically, as shown above?

b. What is the shape of the cross section when the baker slices the bread horizontally?

Big Ideas Math: Modeling Real Life Grade 7 Advanced
Student Journal

E.6 **Cross Sections of Three-Dimensional Figures** (continued)

   c. What is the shape of the cross section when the baker slices off a corner of the bread?

   d. Is it possible to obtain a cross section that is a trapezoid? Explain.

   e. Name at least 3 cross sections that are possible to obtain from a rectangular pyramid. Explain your reasoning.

E.6 Notetaking with Vocabulary

Vocabulary:

Notes:

E.6 Self-Assessment

Use the scale below to rate your understanding of the learning target and the success criteria.

1	2	3	4
I do not understand.	I can do it with help.	I can do it on my own.	I can teach someone else.

	Rating	Date
E.6 Cross Sections of Three-Dimensional Figures		
Learning Target: Describe the cross sections of a solid.	1 2 3 4	
I can explain the meaning of a cross section.	1 2 3 4	
I can describe cross sections of prisms and pyramids.	1 2 3 4	
I can describe cross sections of cylinders and cones.	1 2 3 4	

E.6 Practice

Describe the intersection of the plane and the solid.

1.

2.

3.

4.

5. Describe the cross section of a plane and a cylinder when the plane is parallel to the base of the cylinder. Draw the solid and the cross section.

6. Describe the cross section of a plane and cone when the plane is perpendicular to the base of the cone and passes through the vertex point of the cone. Draw the solid and the cross section.

Determine whether the given intersection is possible. If so, draw the solid and the cross section.

7. The intersection of a plane and a sphere is a point.

8. The intersection of a plane and a cylinder is a triangle.

9. The intersection of a plane and a cylinder is a rectangle.

10. The intersection of a plane and a triangular pyramid is a square.

Name_____ Date_____

Use the scale below to rate your understanding of the learning target and the success criteria.

1 I do not understand. **2** I can do it with help. **3** I can do it on my own. **4** I can teach someone else.

	Rating	Date
E.1 Surface Areas of Prisms		
Learning Target: Find the surface area of a prism.	1 2 3 4	
I can use a formula to find the surface area of a prism.	1 2 3 4	
I can find the lateral surface area of a prism.	1 2 3 4	
E.2 Surface Areas of Cylinders		
Learning Target: Find the surface area of a cylinder.	1 2 3 4	
I can use a formula to find the surface area of a cylinder.	1 2 3 4	
I can find the lateral surface area of a cylinder.		
E.3 Surface Areas of Pyramids		
Learning Target: Find the surface area of a pyramid.	1 2 3 4	
I can use a net to find the surface area of a regular pyramid.	1 2 3 4	
I can find the lateral surface area of a regular pyramid.	1 2 3 4	
E.4 Volumes of Prisms		
Learning Target: Find the volume of a prism.	1 2 3 4	
I can use a formula to find the volume of a prism.	1 2 3 4	
I can use the formula for the volume of a prism to find a missing dimension.	1 2 3 4	

Name _____ Date _____

	Rating	Date
E.5 Volumes of Pyramids		
Learning Target: Find the volume of a pyramid.	1 2 3 4	
I can use a formula to find the volume of a pyramid.	1 2 3 4	
I can use the volume of a pyramid to solve a real-life problem.	1 2 3 4	
E.6 Cross Sections of Three-Dimensional Figures		
Learning Target: Describe the cross sections of a solid.	1 2 3 4	
I can explain the meaning of a cross section.	1 2 3 4	
I can describe cross sections of prisms and pyramids.	1 2 3 4	
I can describe cross sections of cylinders and cones.	1 2 3 4	

Photo Credits

187 *a.* Tom C Amon/Shutterstock.com,
b. Olga Gabay/Shutterstock.com;
c. Tom C Amon/Shutterstock.com;
d. HuHu/Shutterstock.com;
286 ©iStockphoto.com/Joe Potato Photo;
287 *top* Meral Hydaverdi/Shutterstock.com,
bottom Warren Goldswain/Shutterstock.com

Cover Image briddy_/iStock/Getty Images Plus

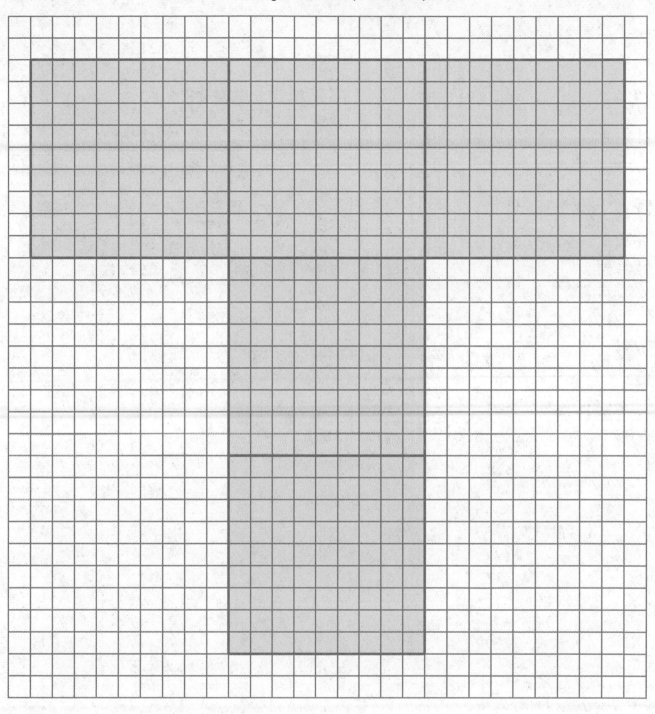

*Available at *BigIdeasMath.com.*

Big Ideas Math: Modeling Real Life Grade 7 Advanced   **381**
Student Journal

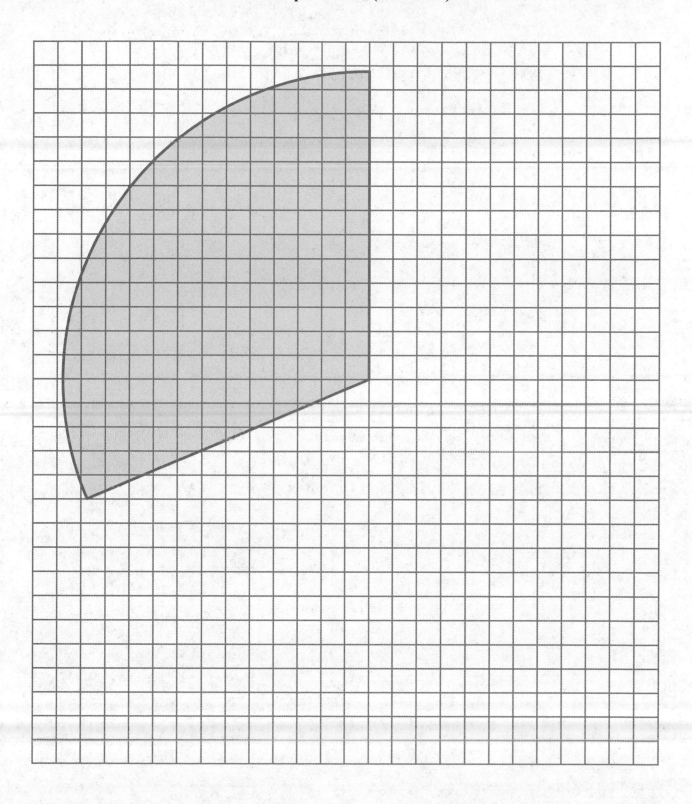

Big Ideas Math: Modeling Real Life Grade 7 Advanced **385**
Student Journal

Spinner 2

*Available at *BigIdeasMath.com.*

*Available at *BigIdeasMath.com*.*

*Available at *BigIdeasMath.com.*

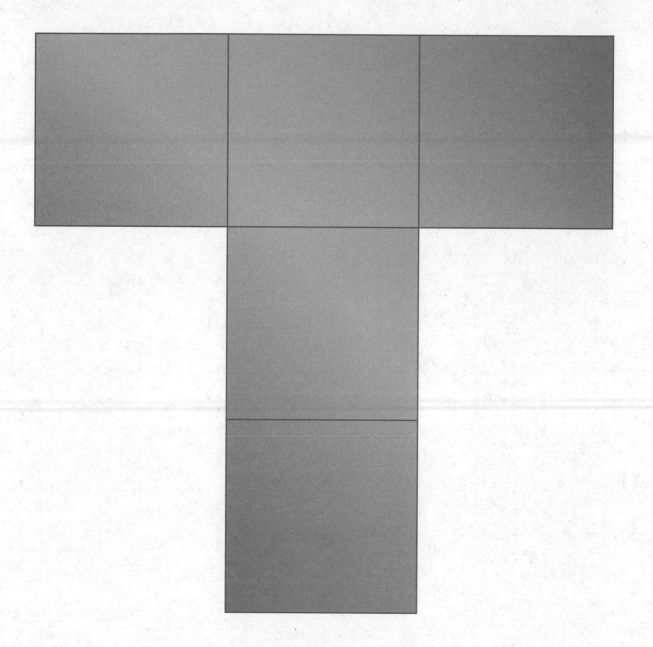

Big Ideas Math: Modeling Real Life Grade 7 Advanced
Student Journal

Algebra Tiles*

*Available at *BigIdeasMath.com*.

Big Ideas Math: Modeling Real Life Grade 7 Advanced

Algebra Tiles (continued)*

*Available at *BigIdeasMath.com*.